THE ULTIMATE
LSU TIGERS
TRIVIA BOOK

A Collection of Amazing Trivia Quizzes
and Fun Facts for Die-Hard Tigers Fans!

Ray Walker

Exclusive Free Book

Crazy Sports Stories

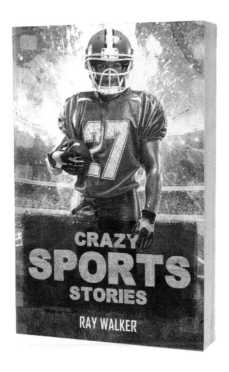

As a thank you for getting a copy of this book I would like to offer you a free copy of my book Crazy Sports Stories which comes packed with interesting stories from your favorite sports such as Football, Hockey, Baseball, Basketball and more.

Grab your free copy over at
RayWalkerMedia.com/Bonus

CONTENTS

INTRODUCTION

When Louisiana State University played its first football game on November 25, 1893, no one knew how much the sport's popularity would blow up over the next century. The 34-0 loss was not the best start for the program, but the LSU Tigers have been one of the most feared teams in college football for over the last half century. Four national championships and plenty more Southeastern Conference championships have cemented LSU's legacy as one of college football's premier programs. And that allure has only grown after the Tigers' championship in 2019, when LSU dominated everyone in their path thanks to quarterback Joe Burrow.

This trivia book covers the entire history of the LSU Tigers program from the fateful day in 1893 through the 2020 season. All of the highs, the occasional lows, and everything in between are fair game to be included in this book. We are going to quiz you on all of your favorite players and coaches over the next 12 chapters of fun facts and interesting nuggets, with the goal that you will finish this book knowing much more about your beloved Tigers than when you took it off your shelf. If we're successful, then we are going to test you and expand your mind and knowledge about LSU football.

1

This book is designed to be a little difficult, and to keep you on the edge of your seat as you engage with the questions and facts. Each chapter focuses on a specific topic, from the history of the program to specific positions, and even the record book. In each chapter, there are 20 multiple-choice or true or false questions, with the answers on a separate page, followed by 10 interesting tidbits about that chapter's topic that will hopefully shed some light on behind-the-scenes information. So please do not be alarmed if some of these questions stump you, the whole point of the book is to help you learn more about your favorite team, so don't expect to ace every chapter.

We want you to learn something new while devouring this book, so that you can use your newfound knowledge to show off to your fellow fans on the bayou. All of the information conveyed in this book is current as of the end of the 2020 season, so be warned that you might know more about the future by the time you pick up this book. All you need to do now is sit back, relax, and enjoy the hours of fun this book provides for the biggest LSU Tigers fans in the world.

CHAPTER 1:

ORIGINS & HISTORY

QUIZ TIME!

1. Who was LSU's first opponent in 1893?

    a. Mississippi

    b. Natchez Athletic Club

    c. Tulane

    d. Louisiana YMCA

2. What was the first conference LSU joined when it began playing college football?

    a. Southwestern Intercollege Athletic Association

    b. Southern Intercollegiate Athletic Association

    c. Southeastern Intercollegiate Athletic Association

    d. Louisiana Intercollegiate Athletic Association

3. Who was the first coach in LSU's history?

    a. Charles Coates

    b. Allen Jeardeau

    c. Albert Simmons

    d. Ruffin Pleasant

4. A win over Alabama in 1895 was the first time LSU played against a school currently in the SEC.

   a. True
   b. False

5. In which year did LSU win 10 games in a season for the first time in program history?

   a. 1908
   b. 1913
   c. 1916
   d. 1922

6. LSU has played at least one football game in every season since 1893 except one. In which year did the Tigers suspend their season?

   a. 1917
   b. 1918
   c. 1944
   d. 1945

7. Who was LSU's first official SEC opponent when the Tigers joined the conference for the 1933 season?

   a. Mississippi State
   b. Arkansas
   c. Tulane
   d. Vanderbilt

8. When was the first night game in Tiger Stadium's history played?

   a. 1928
   b. 1929

c. 1930

d. 1931

9. Tulane was the first ranked opponent LSU ever played.

   a. True

   b. False

10. Where did LSU make its debut in the Associated Press poll during the 1936 season?

    a. 21

    b. 18

    c. 13

    d. 7

11. When was the first time LSU reached No. 1 in the Associated Press poll?

    a. 1939

    b. 1946

    c. 1958

    d. 1963

12. LSU was never ranked No. 1 in the country by the Associated Press from 1959 to 2007.

    a. True

    b. False

13. What was the only No. 1 team that LSU has defeated in the regular season?

    a. Alabama

    b. Auburn

c. Florida

d. Georgia

14. Which school was the last team ever to tie LSU, with a 20-20 draw, in 1995?

    a. Auburn

    b. South Carolina

    c. Mississippi

    d. Tennessee

15. Which team was the opponent in 1998 when LSU played its first overtime game?

    a. Mississippi

    b. Mississippi State

    c. Arkansas

    d. South Carolina

16. How many times has LSU won the SEC championship?

    a. 10

    b. 11

    c. 12

    d. 13

17. When was the only time LSU lost the SEC Championship game?

    a. 1996

    b. 1997

    c. 2002

    d. 2005

18. Which school has LSU beaten the most in program history?

    a. Tulane
    b. Mississippi State
    c. Arkansas
    d. Mississippi

19. Alabama holds the record for most wins over LSU.

    a. True
    b. False

20. Which Mike served the longest as LSU's live mascot?

    a. Mike V
    b. Mike IV
    c. Mike III
    d. Mike I

QUIZ ANSWERS

1. C – Tulane

2. B – Southern Intercollegiate Athletic Association

3. A – Charles Coates

4. B – False

5. A – 1908

6. B – 1918

7. D – Vanderbilt

8. D – 1931

9. A – True

10. C – 13

11. C – 1958

12. A – True

13. C – Florida

14. B – South Carolina

15. A – Mississippi

16. C – 12

17. D – 2005

18. B – Mississippi State

19. A – True

20. D – Mike I

DID YOU KNOW?

1. The Tigers nickname comes partly from the army battalions that represented Louisiana during the Civil War, which were called the Louisiana Tigers. As the team's first coach, Charles Coates, pointed out in an article, every single team in the late 19th century had a vicious mascot name and the purple and gold colors reminded him of a Tiger. The fact that it also paid homage to the state's rich heritage only added to the allure of the nickname.

2. LSU's first coach, Dr. Charles Coates, arrived in Baton Rouge as the school's third faculty member ever to hold a Ph.D. He had played college football at Johns Hopkins and was a natural choice to lead the football program when he discovered there were no athletics on campus upon his arrival. Off the field, however, Coates made a significant impact at LSU as the dean of the Audubon Sugar School as well as the head of LSU's Chemistry Department from 1903 to 1937. His family name is still on several buildings around LSU's campus for his academic success at the school.

3. Much like the first coach in LSU history, the first quarterback in program history was more successful off the field than he was on it. After playing in the 1893 game against Tulane, Ruffin Pleasant studied law at Harvard and Yale before returning to Louisiana and serving as the Shreveport city attorney for six years. He was then an assistant attorney

general in Louisiana for two years before being elected attorney general in 1912. Four years later, Pleasant was elected governor of Louisiana and served one term before returning to a successful law career.

4. Samuel Marmaduke Dinwiddie Clark scored the first touchdown in LSU history in 1894 during the Tigers' win over Natchez Athletic Club. Not much is known about the touchdown or the game except that LSU won 26-0 and Clark, who was also the team captain, scored the opening touchdown.

5. In 1907, LSU played a game in Cuba against the University of Havana, which had dominated the American military teams that had come to play the local college. However, LSU played a far different brand of football and walked away with an easy 56-0 win over the hosts with its finesse and athleticism.

6. LSU has had a live tiger mascot at all of its home games since 1936 when Mike I debuted after being purchased from the Little Rock Zoo for $750. Mike is named after LSU athletic trainer Mike Chambers, who was at the school when the tiger was purchased. Mike I was housed at the Baton Rouge Zoo for the first year before a permanent enclosure was built on campus. For more than 50 years, Mike's cage was placed next to the visiting locker room in preparation for the pregame parade on the field, adding a sense of fear for opponents entering the locker room. Mike I's 20-year run as the LSU Tiger mascot is the longest of all seven Mikes.

Mike VII is the current live tiger mascot, and he took over in the 2017 season.

7. LSU faced off against Spring Hill, a current Division II school in Mobile, Alabama, for its first-ever night game at Tiger Stadium on October 3, 1931. The Tigers won the game 35-0 while wearing purple uniforms with white numerals, designed to reflect the light and illuminate the players for the fans in attendance. Two of the major reasons behind the evening games were avoiding conflicts with Tulane and Loyola in New Orleans and allowing many of the fans and alumni in the agriculture industry to attend games.

8. LSU plays for potentially the heaviest trophy in college football every year when it faces Arkansas for the Golden Boot. The 24-karat gold trophy weighs nearly 200 pounds and the golden map of Louisiana and Arkansas is valued at around $10,000. The trophy came into existence before the 1996 season and the Tigers have gone home with the trophy 17 times in the 25 seasons since its introduction.

9. One of the most famous games in LSU lore is the Earthquake Game of 1988, when a last-minute touchdown pass helped the Tigers stun No. 4 Auburn at Tiger Stadium. LSU faced fourth-and-10 at the Auburn 11-yard line with less than two minutes left, when Tommy Hodson threw a touchdown pass to Eddie Fuller to complete a 7-6 win over the other Tigers. The reaction from the more than 79,000 fans in attendance was so loud and boisterous that the LSU Department of Geology registered the vibrations emanating from the stadium as an earthquake.

10. LSU is 201-116-4 in nationally televised games on CBS and the ABC/ESPN family of networks. The Tigers are 75-29 on ESPN, 53-45-1 on CBS, 21-33-3 on ABC, 16-1 on ESPNU, 19-6 on ESPN2 and 17-2 on the newly created SEC Network. In addition, LSU is 21-12 when they are playing in the game hosting ESPN's College Gameday that week.

CHAPTER 2:

NUMBERS GAME

QUIZ TIME!

1. What color were the uniforms that LSU wore in its first game, which were adorned with the purple and gold ribbons that became the school colors?

   a. White
   b. Gray
   c. Black
   d. Blue

2. In which season did LSU change its helmet to the familiar shade of gold?

   a. 1952
   b. 1954
   c. 1956
   d. 1958

3. Which coach led the charge for the Tigers to wear white at home, seeking to appeal the NCAA rule requiring schools to wear dark colors at home?

a. Gerry DiNardo

b. Jerry Stovall

c. Mike Archer

d. Curley Hallman

4. Which school was not one of the opponents against which LSU has worn gold jerseys since 1995?

a. Vanderbilt

b. Florida

c. Notre Dame

d. Mississippi

5. Nick Saban started the tradition of LSU wearing purple jerseys at home for all non-SEC games that weren't home openers.

a. True

b. False

6. Which of these numbers has not been retired by LSU?

a. 20

b. 21

c. 27

d. 37

7. What number did Warren Rabb wear in 1958 when quarterbacking LSU to its first national championship?

a. 9

b. 10

c. 11

d. 12

8. What number did Y.A. Tittle wear during his time leading the Tigers from 1944 to 1947?

   a. 23
   b. 25
   c. 27
   d. 29

9. Which number was not worn by one of the five former Tigers players in the Pro Football Hall of Fame?

   a. 34
   b. 39
   c. 42
   d. 52

10. The 2003 national championship squad was led by quarterback Matt Mauck, who began the tradition behind which number at LSU?

    a. 9
    b. 15
    c. 18
    d. 19

11. What number was Marcus Spears wearing when he was dominating opposing offensive lines as a defensive end of that 2003 national championship squad?

    a. 84
    b. 88
    c. 92
    d. 95

12. What number was Glenn Dorsey wearing when he was sweeping every major lineman award during the 2007 national championship season?

    a. 98
    b. 91
    c. 78
    d. 72

13. Former LSU offensive coordinator Steve Ensminger wore what number when he was playing quarterback for LSU?

    a. 1
    b. 2
    c. 4
    d. 5

14. What number did Tommy Hodson wear during his record-breaking career at LSU?

    a. 11
    b. 12
    c. 13
    d. 14

15. Justin Jefferson wore No. 32 as a freshman at LSU because he arrived on campus after fall camp began in his freshman year.

    a. True
    b. False

16. Which number did Kevin Faulk wear during his record-setting career at LSU?

a. 3

b. 5

c. 23

d. 24

17. What number did Dwayne Bowe wear during his college career at LSU?

    a. 80

    b. 82

    c. 84

    d. 88

18. What number did Odell Beckham Jr. wear as a freshman at LSU as a tribute to his father before switching to the familiar No. 3 for this final two years in school?

    a. 5

    b. 22

    c. 27

    d. 33

19. What number did Jamal Adams wear at LSU before becoming a first-round pick in 2017?

    a. 33

    b. 27

    c. 22

    d. 18

20. Every player to wear No. 7 since Patrick Peterson left LSU has been drafted in the first round of the NFL draft.

    a. True

    b. False

QUIZ ANSWERS

1. B – Gray

2. C – 1956

3. A – Gerry DiNardo

4. D – Mississippi

5. A – True

6. C – 27

7. D – 12

8. B – 25

9. B – 39

10. C – 18

11. A – 84

12. D – 72

13. D – 5

14. C – 13

15. A – True

16. A – 3

17. A – 80

18. D – 33

19. A – 33

20. B – False

DID YOU KNOW?

1. The purple and gold that we have come to associate with LSU was a mere happy accident in the lead-up to the team's first game. Coach Charles Coates and quarterback Ruff Pleasant went shopping for colored ribbons to adorn the team's uniform. The store was out of green ribbon but had plenty of purple and gold because it was stocking up for Mardi Gras in a few months. The pair bought plenty of those two colors and liked the way the colors looked, so they have stuck right to the present day with few tweaks.

2. The tradition of LSU wearing white jerseys at home began with the 1958 national championship squad, which wore white uniforms at home for the first time that season. The tradition stayed in place until the NCAA mandated in 1982 that the home team wear the darker colored uniform. For 12 seasons, LSU did not wear its trademark whites at home but that changed when Gerry DiNardo became the Tigers' coach in 1995 and vowed to appeal the NCAA's ruling. The rule was changed to requiring that the visiting team must consent to the lighter uniform color. The SEC eventually stepped in, though, and gave the home team the sole discretion of choosing uniform colors.

3. In 1952, LSU coach Gus Tinsley adopted a unique system for uniform numbers that did not last long at all in Baton Rouge. The coach, who boldly claimed the system would

"revolutionize" the jersey manufacturing industry, had each member of the offense wear a letter corresponding to their position followed by a single-digit number. The right side of the lines wore even numbers and the left wore odd numbers, but the numbers were quickly changed back to the old method still in place today.

4. There are a few honored jersey numbers at LSU. The most recent one to enter the pantheon is No. 7. After Patrick Peterson dominated in that number from 2008 through 2010, the Tigers started a tradition of handing the number to the next great playmaker at the school. Tyrann Mathieu, Leonard Fournette, D.J. Chark, Grant Delpit, and Ja'Marr Chase have all worn the No. 7 for the Tigers since Peterson's departure.

5. The players have a larger say in who will wear the coveted No. 18, as they all vote in the preseason. The jersey has become a symbol of on- and off-field success after Matt Mauck led the Tigers to the 2003 national championship wearing that uniform number. It has become an important tradition for players to be given the number after notable stars Tre'Davious White and Jacob Hester wore it for the Tigers.

6. It was an easy decision for LSU to retire Billy Cannon's No. 20 after his performances in 1958 and 1959. Cannon helped lead the Tigers to a national championship in 1958, and then became the school's first Heisman Trophy winner in 1959. It didn't even take a full season for LSU to retire Cannon's No.

20 and prevent any other LSU football player from ever wearing the historic number again.

7. Tommy Casanova's No. 37 was retired in 2009, almost 50 years after Cannon's No. 20 was taken out of circulation by the school. Casanova is LSU's only three-time first-team All-American and he contributed to all three facets of the game during his time in Baton Rouge, though notably he was an ace returner for the Tigers. He returned two punts for a touchdown in 1970 against Mississippi and was on the cover of *Sports Illustrated*'s 1971 college football preview issue as a potential Heisman Trophy favorite. Casanova spent six seasons in the NFL with the Bengals, but a knee problem forced him to retire, and he finished the medical degree he began while in the NFL. He also later served in the Louisiana State Senate from 1996 to 2000.

8. The third number retired by LSU was Jerry Stovall's No. 21, though that came in 2018, more than 50 years after he last played for the Tigers. Stovall was the runner-up for the Heisman in 1962 as another do-everything player for LSU, including punting. Stovall also later returned to Baton Rouge as the head coach for four seasons, and was named the national coach of the year during one of his seasons in charge.

9. As a freshman in 2011, Odell Beckham Jr. paid homage to his father by wearing No. 33, the same number his father wore at the school. However, the younger Beckham changed his number for his sophomore and junior seasons as a way to

make a name for himself at the school. Beckham Jr. said that his father was proud of him regardless of his number and that he kept a No. 33 jersey at home as a keepsake for his father.

10. You can thank wide receiver Stephen Sullivan for Joe Burrow wearing the No. 9 during his two seasons in Baton Rouge. Burrow wore No. 10 for most of his football career, but the number wasn't available when he transferred from Ohio State to LSU, so he settled on No. 9.

CHAPTER 3:

CALLING THE SIGNALS

QUIZ TIME!

1. Which LSU quarterback won the most games as the Tigers'
   starter?

   a. JaMarcus Russell

   b. Joe Burrow

   c. Warren Rabb

   d. Tommy Hodson

2. Which quarterback did not win every game in a single
   season while starting more than half of LSU's games?

   a. Tommy Hodson

   b. Joe Burrow

   c. Jarratt Lee

   d. Warren Rabb

3. Who is not one of the eight quarterbacks to win at least 20
   games for LSU?

   a. Jordan Jefferson

   b. Jimmy Field

c. Jeff Wickersham

d. Zach Mettenberger

4. Josh Booty is the last LSU quarterback to have a losing record in a single season in which he made multiple starts.

a. True

b. False

5. Who is not one of the five LSU quarterbacks to rush for three touchdowns in a single game?

a. Alan Risher

b. Herb Tyler

c. Paul Lyons

d. David Woodley

6. Who is the only quarterback in LSU history to rush for 1,000 yards in his career?

a. JaMarcus Russell

b. David Woodley

c. Jordan Jefferson

d. Lee Hedges

7. Which quarterback never had a 400-yard passing game for LSU during his career in Baton Rouge?

a. Joe Burrows

b. JaMarcus Russell

c. Tommy Hodson

d. Rohan Davey

8. What was LSU's record for passing touchdowns in a season before Joe Burrow obliterated it in 2019?

a. 28

b. 31

c. 34

d. 38

9. How long was Joe Burrow's school-record streak of consecutive passing attempts without an interception in 2019?

a. 159

b. 163

c. 174

d. 187

10. Y.A. Tittle threw a longer pass during his LSU career than Joe Burrow.

a. True

b. False

11. How many points was Joe Burrow responsible for during his historic 2019 season?

a. 289

b. 343

c. 392

d. 410

12. How many times did Joe Burrow throw for five touchdowns or more during the 2019 season?

a. 5

b. 6

c. 7

d. 8

13. Joe Burrow threw enough touchdown passes in 2019 to set the LSU career record.

    a. True
    b. False

14. Who was the opponent when Rohan Davey set the LSU record for completions and passing yards in a game during the 2001 season?

    a. Alabama
    b. Auburn
    c. Mississippi
    d. Arkansas

15. Which quarterback is one of three to have attempted 50 passes in a game for LSU?

    a. Tommy Hodson
    b. Rohan Davey
    c. Josh Booty
    d. Joe Burrow

16. Who is the only quarterback to complete every pass he attempted with a minimum of 10 attempts?

    a. Herb Tyler
    b. Tommy Hodson
    c. Warren Rabb
    d. Rohan Davey

17. Who threw the longest non-scoring pass in LSU history?

    a. Matt Mauck
    b. Jamie Howard

c. Anthony Jennings

d. Steve Ensminger

18. In which country was Rohan Davey born?

    a. Canada

    b. Jamaica

    c. Haiti

    d. United States

19. Tommy Hodson still holds LSU's career record for passing yards record despite Joe Burrow's 2019 season.

    a. True

    b. False

20. Who held the LSU record for passing touchdowns in a game before Joe Burrow arrived in Baton Rouge?

    a. Matt Flynn

    b. Herb Tyler

    c. Zach Mettenberg

    d. Rohan Davey

QUIZ ANSWERS

1. D – Tommy Hodson

2. A – Tommy Hodson

3. D – Zach Mettenberger

4. B – False

5. A – Alan Risher

6. C – Jordan Jefferson

7. B – JaMarcus Russell

8. A – 28

9. D – 187

10. A – True

11. C – 392

12. B – 6

13. B – False

14. A – Alabama

15. C – Josh Booty

16. D – Rohan Davey

17. D – Steve Ensminger

18. B – Jamaica

19. A – True

20. C – Zach Mettenberger

DID YOU KNOW?

1. Warren Rabb won 25 games over three seasons as the LSU starting quarterback, a record for wins that lasted nearly 40 years in Baton Rouge. Rabb had the benefit of an excellent rushing attack, so he threw for only 1,030 yards in his career, almost half of which came during the 1958 championship season. In fact, the 505 yards he threw for in that game is only 23 yards shy of the LSU team record for passing yards in a game.

2. Jimmy Field succeeded Rabb as LSU's starting quarterback. He led the Tigers to a 10-1 record in 1961 and won 8 of his 10 starts the following year. He had a very busy week leading into the 1962 game against TCU after he got married and had his first child. Field scored the only touchdown in the 1963 Cotton Bowl against Texas to propel LSU to an unofficial national championship after being crowned as such by the Berryman Quality Point Rating System.

3. Steve Ensminger played quarterback at LSU under the legendary Charles McClendon, but he is perhaps equally as known for his 11 seasons on staff at LSU as an assistant coach. He began as the team's tight ends coach before becoming the interim offensive coordinator in 2016, and livening up an underperforming offense in the eight games in his charge. The Tigers had scored just nine touchdowns and were averaging 18 points per game in the first four

games of the 2016 season. In eight games with Ensminger calling the plays, LSU averaged 32 points and 464.9 total yards per contest. Ensminger also was the architect of the 2019 offense that broke numerous records en route to the national title.

4. It might be a while before someone touches Tommy Hodson's school record of 31 wins as a starting quarterback. Hodson was a four-year starter who held most of LSU's career passing records before Joe Burrow. He was a four-time All-SEC quarterback – three times as the first-team quarterback – and was the SEC Rookie of the Year in 1986 as a redshirt freshman. He has said in interviews that he was in the right place at the right time that season as a younger player on an experienced team and that is what helped the Tigers reach the Sugar Bowl that season.

5. Herb Tyler may rank second in LSU history for total victories, but he had arguably the most impressive regular season win in the program's history. It was Tyler who led the Tigers to their only regular season win over a top-ranked team, defeating Florida 28-21 on October 11, 1997, at Tiger Stadium. Tyler opened the scoring with a 40-yard touchdown run midway through the first quarter and added the eventual winning touchdown in the fourth quarter on a run from 11 yards out. Tyler ran for 50 yards on eight carries and completed 10 of his 17 passing attempts for an additional 172 yards in the victory.

6. In the 20 years since the record was set, no one has yet touched the day Rohan Davey had on November 3, 2001, in

Tuscaloosa, Alabama. Facing a hated rival like Alabama, Davey uncorked the greatest passing performance in school history with a school-record 528 yards while completing a record 35 passes on just 44 attempts. Many of Davey's career passing records have been eclipsed in the years since that game, but his single-game records are safe for now thanks to his heroic performance against the Crimson Tide.

7. When Matt Mauck stepped in to beat Tennessee in the 2001 SEC Championship game, he was technically a walk-on quarterback. Mauck had originally committed to play football and baseball at Michigan State under Nick Saban but decided to try his hand at pro baseball instead, after being drafted by the Chicago Cubs. He missed football too much, though, and decided to return to the gridiron as a 21-year-old freshman for Saban at LSU. However, he wasn't using up a scholarship because minor league baseball was paying his LSU tuition for the first five semesters.

8. JaMarcus Russell was a clear flop in the NFL, but there was no doubting his natural skill on the football field. He won 25 of his 29 starts at LSU and wowed fans with his accuracy, arm strength, and speed. He still ranks third in school history in completion percentage, passing efficiency, and passing touchdowns while ranking fourth in passing yards. His 28 passing touchdowns in 2006 was the standard before Joe Burrow broke the record.

9. Zach Mettenberger arrived at LSU in 2011 with a checkered past from his previous stops. He had been in a competition with Aaron Murray to start at Georgia, but he was cut from

the team for sexual battery charges to which he later plead guilty to. That took him to a junior college where he rehabbed his image and threw for 2,600 yards and 32 touchdowns, with only four interceptions. He matured over that span and led LSU to 19 wins in two seasons, before his college career ended with a knee injury in the 2013 season finale.

10. Joe Burrow arrived in Baton Rouge in May 2018 for a recruiting visit, unaware of how the next 48 hours would inevitably change his life. Burrow elected to transfer from Ohio State after three years as the backup and LSU was one of just two schools he visited. Many assumed he would end up at Cincinnati in his home state of Ohio but, after 48 hours of film study and conversation, Burrow signed on at LSU. Just 18 months later, Burrow was leading the Tigers to one of the greatest seasons in college football history and the program's fourth national championship.

CHAPTER 4:

BETWEEN THE TACKLES

QUIZ TIME!

1. Who is the only LSU running back to rush 40 times in a game?

    a. Charles Alexander

    b. Kevin Faulk

    c. Billy Cannon

    d. Leonard Fournette

2. How many times has an LSU running back rushed for 200 yards in a game?

    a. 15

    b. 17

    c. 19

    d. 21

3. When Leonard Fournette tied the LSU record for consecutive 100-yard games at nine, how many consecutive times did he rush for 200 yards in a game during that stretch?

a. 2

b. 3

c. 4

d. 5

4. With whom does Fournette share the record for most consecutive 100-yard performances?

    a. Derrius Guice

    b. Kevin Faulk

    c. Charles Alexander

    d. Joseph Addai

5. How quickly did Leonard Fournette rush for 1,000 yards in his record-breaking 2015 season?

    a. 4 games

    b. 5 games

    c. 6 games

    d. 7 games

6. Leonard Fournette ran for more yards in 2015 than Billy Cannon had in his entire LSU career.

    a. True

    b. False

7. Kevin Faulk holds the career rushing record at LSU. How many times did he rush for 100 yards in a game during his time in Baton Rouge?

    a. 20

    b. 22

    c. 24

    d. 26

8. Who did LSU play in 1997 when Kevin Faulk set the single-game record with five rushing touchdowns?

    a. Texas Tech

    b. Tulane

    c. Kentucky

    d. Auburn

9. How long was Derrius Guice's school-record rushing touchdown in 2016 against Arkansas?

    a. 88 yards

    b. 90 yards

    c. 93 yards

    d. 96 yards

10. Derrius Guice holds three of the top-four single-game rushing totals in LSU history.

    a. True

    b. False

11. Who is not one of the three LSU running backs to rush for 4,000 yards in his career?

    a. Charles Alexander

    b. Dalton Hilliard

    c. Kevin Faulk

    d. Leonard Fournette

12. Who holds the record for most career rushes at LSU?

    a. Derrius Guice

    b. Charles Alexander

    c. Harvey Williams

    d. Dalton Hilliard

13. Kevin Faulk was never a first-team All-American at running back.

    a. True
    b. False

14. How many kickoffs and punts did Kevin Faulk return for a touchdown in his career?

    a. 2
    b. 3
    c. 4
    d. 5

15. Which other award did Billy Cannon not win during his 1959 Heisman Trophy-winning campaign?

    a. Associated Press Player of the Year
    b. Walter Camp Trophy
    c. Doak Walker Award
    d. SEC Player of the Year

16. Who is the only other running back besides Billy Cannon to be a first-team All-American in consecutive seasons?

    a. Leonard Fournette
    b. Charles Alexander
    c. Jerry Stovall
    d. Jimmy Taylor

17. LSU did not have two 100-yard rushers against Oregon in 1977 when it set the school record for rushing yards in a game.

    a. True
    b. False

18. Who was the first Tigers running back to rush for 250 yards in a game?

    a. Terry Robiskie
    b. Leonard Fournette
    c. Alley Broussard
    d. Derrius Guice

19. Who was the first LSU running back to rush for 1,000 yards in a season?

    a. Dalton Hilliard
    b. Charles Alexander
    c. Terry Robiskie
    d. Harvey Williams

20. Which of these LSU greats did not hail from Louisiana originally?

    a. Kevin Faulk
    b. Billy Cannon
    c. Jerry Stovall
    d. Charles Alexander

QUIZ ANSWERS

1. A – Charles Alexander

2. D – 21

3. C – 3

4. C – Charles Alexander

5. B – 5 games

6. A – True

7. B – 22

8. C – Kentucky

9. D – 96 yards

10. A – True

11. D – Leonard Fournette

12. D – Dalton Hilliard

13. A – True

14. B – 3

15. C – Doak Walker Award

16. B – Charles Alexander

17. A – True

18. C – Alley Broussard

19. C – Terry Robiskie

20. D – Charles Alexander

DID YOU KNOW?

1. It is impossible to mention Billy Cannon without talking about the Halloween Run. Cannon's famous 89-yard punt return on Halloween 1959 was the only touchdown in LSU's 7-3 win over No. 3 Mississippi that kept the Tigers No. 1 in the country for another week. Through the fog that sat on top of Tiger Stadium that night, Cannon fielded a bouncing ball and sprinted up the sidelines. He evaded seven futile defenders as he darted in a straight line into the end zone, and some may argue he won the Heisman Trophy that night in Baton Rouge.

2. Jerry Stovall also had a very memorable moment for LSU against Mississippi with a 57-yard touchdown run in 1961 that helped the Tigers upend the undefeated Rebels 10-7. Unlike Cannon, though, Stovall could not parlay that run into a national award as he finished second in the Heisman voting the following season. Just three years after Cannon's win, some teammates said the voters just didn't want to give the award to another LSU running back. Stovall led the Tigers in rushing and receiving that season as LSU finished No. 7 in the country and beat Texas in the Cotton Bowl.

3. Only three times in LSU's history has a running back had 40 or more rushing attempts in a game and all three were accomplished by Charles Alexander during the 1977 and 1978 seasons. The College Football Hall of Famer held the

LSU rushing record for 38 years after running for 1,686 yards in 1977, averaging more than 150 yards per game for the first time in school history. He set nine SEC records during that 1977 campaign, and he tied a 10th record while being named the conference's MVP.

4. Dalton Hilliard was a star back for the Tigers in the mid-1980s and still ranks second on LSU's all-time rushing list. Hilliard also ranks second in rushing touchdowns and became the second running back in program history to have two 1,000-yard seasons. Many more recent fans of LSU, though, might be more familiar with his nephew, Kenny, who burst onto the scene as a freshman in 2011 before getting buried on the depth chart in later seasons.

5. Kevin Faulk returned to his alma mater in 2018 as the director of player development before being promoted in February 2020 to running backs coach. He is now tasked with grooming the players who are attacking his school rushing records. Faulk still holds the school record for rushing yards and rushing touchdowns during his four years in Baton Rouge. He had a school-record 22 games rushing for 100 yards or more and he had three 1,000-yard seasons for the Tigers during his time in the backfield from 1995 to 1998, graduating with the SEC record for all-purpose yards.

6. When Joseph Addai came to LSU as a freshman running back, he requested that his dorm room be wheelchair accessible. It was a strange request for a fairly healthy

running back, but Addai wanted to make sure his friend LaJuan Moore would be able to visit him in Baton Rouge. Moore was a star on Addai's high school football team, but a freak accident during a tackle left Moore paralyzed. Moore visited almost every gameday weekend and had already become a household name for those who knew Addai, before he even stepped on campus. Moore's struggles were another reason Addai stuck it out at LSU despite limited playing time, and then he exploded onto the scene as a senior in 2005.

7. Jacob Hester came up with some of the biggest plays of the 2007 season for LSU with his grit and determination on the ground. Three of them came in the same game on October 6, 2007, when the Tigers hosted Florida, the defending national champion, in a primetime game at Tiger Stadium. Hester converted a pair of critical fourth downs, including one by the slightest nose of the football, and then scored the game-winning touchdown with just over a minute left to keep LSU's perfect season alive. When reflecting on those fourth-down conversions, Hester said, "I honestly felt like I got every one of them. ... I know at first glance it didn't look like we got it. Luckily enough, I got some forward lean and we barely got it. Gosh, they were all close. ... It was a pretty special night on a pretty special year."

8. Leonard Fournette was already hyped up pretty hard when he arrived at LSU as a freshman. The Louisiana native had become a local legend for his performances at the Pop Warner and high school levels but, on October 22, 2016, he became the star attraction when he set the LSU single-game

rushing record against Mississippi. Fournette had been playing on a sprained ankle most of the season but that didn't slow him down as he ran for 284 yards, and three touchdowns, on just 16 carries that day against the Rebels.

9. The 2016 season was special for Fournette and Derrius Guice, as they combined to set the top three single-game rushing totals in LSU history. Guice set the record with 285 yards against Texas A&M on November 24, one yard more than Fournette had run for against Mississippi the previous month. Guice ran for 252 against Arkansas on November 12 and he broke that record with 276 yards against Mississippi on October 21, 2017.

10. Clyde Edwards-Helaire was named for his father, Clyde Edwards Sr., but his parents were split up when his father was arrested and indicted on charges of cocaine possession. He was convicted and sentenced to jail time and Edwards-Helaire's mother married Shannon Helaire in 2002. When he was 14, the younger Clyde legally changed his name to Clyde Edwards-Helaire to honor both his father and stepfather, who became his father figure while his biological dad was in jail.

CHAPTER 5:

CATCHING THE BALL

QUIZ TIME!

1. By how many yards did Josh Reed surpass 3,000 receiving yards during his LSU career?

   a. 1
   b. 7
   c. 12
   d. 19

2. How many times did Josh Reed have more than 100 yards receiving in a game during his historic 2001 season?

   a. 8
   b. 9
   c. 11
   d. 12

3. Who did LSU play when Josh Reed set the single-game record for receptions and yards in a game?

   a. Kentucky
   b. Mississippi

c. Alabama

d. Florida

4. Which single-season record did Josh Reed not set during the 2001 season?

   a. Single-season receptions

   b. Single-season touchdowns

   c. Single-season receiving yards

   d. Consecutive 100-yard receiving games

5. Who was the first LSU receiver to reach 1,000 receiving yards in a season?

   a. Michael Clayton

   b. Wendell Davis

   c. Josh Reed

   d. Eric Martin

6. Who was LSU's first receiver to gain over 200 yards in a game?

   a. Sheddrick Wilson

   b. Eric Martin

   c. Carlos Carson

   d. Wendell Davis

7. Who holds the LSU record for most career receptions by a tight end?

   a. Thaddeus Moss

   b. Robert Royal

   c. Mitch Andrews

   d. Richard Dickson

8. Brad Boyd is the only tight end besides Richard Dickson to catch five touchdown passes.

    a. True
    b. False

9. Which record did an LSU receiver not break during the 2019 season?

    a. Single-game touchdowns
    b. Single-season receptions
    c. Single-season touchdowns
    d. Single-season yards

10. The LSU single-game record for yards per catch is 40.2.

    a. True
    b. False

11. In which year was Ken Kavanaugh a consensus All-American as an end?

    a. 1936
    b. 1937
    c. 1938
    d. 1939

12. Although it is no longer in the top 10, how many receptions did Eric Martin have when he set the single-season receptions record in 1983?

    a. 43
    b. 48
    c. 52
    d. 55

13. Who is LSU's only two-time first-team All-American at wide receiver?

    a. Josh Reed
    b. Wendell Davis
    c. Odell Beckham Jr.
    d. Eric Martin

14. Wendell Davis holds the Tiger Stadium record with 14 catches during a game against Mississippi.

    a. True
    b. False

15. How many touchdowns did Dwayne Bowe catch to set the LSU career record?

    a. 22
    b. 24
    c. 26
    d. 28

16. Dwayne Bowe's single-season record for touchdown catches was passed by three different receivers during the 2019 season.

    a. True
    b. False

17. Josh Reed was half of six duos that both had 100 yards in the same game. Who was the other half of the receiving duo the most?

    a. Jarel Myers
    b. Michael Clayton

c. Reggie Robinson

d. Robert Royal

18. Which award did Odell Beckham Jr. win in 2013 as the most versatile player in the nation?

a. Burlsworth Trophy

b. Broyles Award

c. Danny Wuerffel Trophy

d. Paul Hornung Award

19. How many times did Odell Beckham Jr. and Jarvis Landry both go over 100 yards in the same game during their LSU careers?

a. 0

b. 2

c. 3

d. 4

20. LSU's 2019 win over Texas was the only time the Tigers had three 100-yard receivers in the same game. Who was not one of those receivers?

a. Ja'Marr Chase

b. Justin Jefferson

c. Thaddeus Moss

d. Terrace Marshall Jr.

QUIZ ANSWERS

1. A – 1
2. C – 11
3. C – Alabama
4. B – Single-season touchdowns
5. D – Eric Martin
6. C – Carlos Carson
7. D – Richard Dickson
8. B – False
9. A – Single-game touchdowns
10. A – True
11. D – 1939
12. C – 52
13. B – Wendell Davis
14. A – True
15. C – 26
16. A – True
17. B – Michael Clayton
18. D – Paul Hornung Award
19. B – 2
20. C – Thaddeus Moss

DID YOU KNOW?

1. Ken Kavanaugh Sr. was the first receiving threat in LSU history, finishing seventh in the Heisman voting in 1939 as an end for the Tigers. He caught three touchdown passes and ran for a fourth against Holy Cross that season, setting a record for total touchdowns that wouldn't be equaled for almost 40 years and he was a first-team All-American that season. The receiving bloodline was strong in the Kavanaugh family as Ken Kavanaugh Jr. also was a receiver for the Tigers, but he didn't have the same success as his father.

2. Eric Martin arrived at LSU as a running back but was shifted to wide receiver before his sophomore year due to a litany of running backs coming in with the next recruiting class. Despite never having played the position, Martin became a natural with his strong, physical body, and what coach Jerry Stovall described as "the softest hands of any high school athlete I've ever seen." Martin ended up setting the SEC record with 2,625 receiving yards when he graduated in 1984, and he also left the school with the single-game receiving record for yards, the single-season records for catches and yards, and the career record for receptions.

3. Wendell Davis admitted to being a little scared the first time he stepped into Tiger Stadium for a game as an LSU wide receiver. "I was scared out of my mind," Davis recounted in a book put out by *The Advocate*. "I'm not going to lie. I was

scared, excited, and all of those things rolled up into one. (But) once you felt the love of the fans in that atmosphere, it was just electrifying. Every game after that walking into Tiger Stadium, it was not fear. It was more excitement. I loved putting on a show for our fans." Davis certainly put on a show for LSU fans around the country by rewriting the record book in his final three years in Baton Rouge after not catching a single pass as a freshman. He broke all three major single-season receiving records in 1986 as a junior and left the school the following year as the career record-holder in all three categories as well.

4. Josh Reed is another high school running back who converted to wide receiver in Baton Rouge, and he became one of the best ever to play at LSU. In his final year at LSU in 2001, Reed set 17 LSU, SEC, and Sugar Bowl records as part of a dominant season in which he won the Biletnikoff Award as the top receiver in the country. There were two memorable moments from that season for most LSU fans, the 19 catches and 293 yards against Alabama, both of which are still school records, and the 14 catches Reed had against Illinois in the Sugar Bowl that season. The Sugar Bowl beatdown of the Fighting Illini still ranks in the top three at LSU in receptions and yards.

5. Dwayne Bowe didn't play football until he was a junior in high school, but he still made an impact at LSU during his four years. What perhaps stands out the most is the jump Bowe took from his junior year in 2005, when he caught 41 passes for 710 yards to his senior season when he hauled in 65

passes for 990 yards and 12 touchdowns. The difference was all in the eyes as Bowe underwent laser-eye surgery between his junior and senior seasons because he was having trouble playing with contacts. With better vision, Bowe became an even bigger menace for opposing secondaries.

6. Brandon LaFell's LSU career was defined by a series of fascinating decisions. He was a third-string high school quarterback who was sent to play receiver one weekend before his junior year when his teammates were late to a 7-on-7 tournament. LaFell shone that weekend; he was named the MVP and earned his first two scholarship offers. He played his high school football with receiver R.J. Jackson and the two decided in their senior year to go to school together. One night, the two had tickets to the rodeo and they discussed their college options, deciding on LSU. Then, after going over 1,000 yards as a junior, LaFell entered the NFL draft, only to rescind that declaration within the 72-hour window and return to school for a final year.

7. Odell Beckham Jr.'s relationship with LSU has been put on pause for his celebration after the 2019 national championship game. Beckham handed out $2,000 to four members of the team on the field after the game, which is a Level III NCAA violation. In addition to self-imposed sanctions on recruiting due to the incident, LSU also announced that it has barred Beckham from the football facility for two years.

8. When Beckham and Jarvis Landry were teammates on the Cleveland Browns in 2019, Landry bought Beckham a

scooter as a gift. The story behind that present dates back to the two of them being teammates at LSU. Beckham had bought a scooter to help him get around campus easier and Landry needed to get to the football facility for a meeting with a coach. Landry borrowed the scooter and 10 minutes later, he called Beckham to say he was hit by a bus and the scooter was totaled. Landry suffered minor scrapes in the accident, but Beckham said he laughed that Landry's first thought after getting hit by the bus was to freak out about the scooter.

9. Justin Jefferson's historic performance in the 2019 Peach Bowl all began with a few snubs on the awards circuit. Jefferson caught 88 passes for 14 touchdowns and more than 1,200 yards but was not named to the coaches' All-SEC team and was a second-team All-SEC selection by the Associated Press. Oklahoma's CeeDee Lamb was an All-American despite the same number of touchdowns, one more yard, and 30 fewer catches as Jefferson. Fueled by being overlooked, Jefferson practiced angrily the week leading into the Peach Bowl and LSU wide receivers coach Mickey Joseph told media members to watch out for Jefferson. He caught four first-half touchdowns in the win and finished with 14 catches for 227 yards in three quarters of work.

10. LSU literally pooled almost every resource it had to recruit Ja'Marr Chase to stay at home and play at LSU. Chase was down to LSU and Auburn as his final two choices a week before signing day, so coach Ed Orgeron and his entire coaching staff made the trek down to New Orleans in a

limousine bus. Each member of the staff made a pitch to Chase, and Chase's father said that trip was a major reason why he thought his son decided to play for the purple and gold Tigers.

CHAPTER 6:

TRENCH WARFARE

QUIZ TIME!

1. Which center joined Gus Tinsley as a first-team All-American in 1935, making them the first two LSU players to earn the distinction?

   a. Max Fugler

   b. George Tarasovic

   c. Justin Rukas

   d. Marvin Stewart

2. Who was LSU's first winner of the Jacobs Award as the best blocker in the SEC?

   a. Bill May

   b. Sid Fournet

   c. Robert Dugas

   d. Allen Hover

3. Justin Rukas was an All-SEC first-team selection at two different offensive line positions during his LSU career.

a. True

b. False

4. In which year did LSU set its school record for rushing yards in a season?

a. 1976

b. 2007

c. 1977

d. 2015

5. Who was not one of the offensive linemen named a first-team All-American during the four-year stretch between 1962 and 1965 when the Tigers had one lineman named to the team every year?

a. Roy Winston

b. Fred Miller

c. George Rice

d. Billy Truax

6. LSU has had more offensive linemen named first-team All-American than players at offensive skill positions.

a. True

b. False

7. Who was LSU's first finalist for the Outland Trophy?

a. George Rice

b. Lance Smith

c. Glenn Dorsey

d. Alan Faneca

8. Who is the only LSU center to win the Rimington Trophy as college football's best center?

    a. Kevin Mawae

    b. Todd McClure

    c. Ben Wilkerson

    d. Ethan Pocic

9. Who was LSU's most recent first-team All-American on the offensive line?

    a. Lloyd Cushenberry

    b. Will Blackwell

    c. Ethan Pocic

    d. Will Clapp

10. Which team-based award did the 2019 LSU offensive line win after the Tigers won the national championship?

    a. Harvey Mudd Award

    b. Joe Moore Award

    c. Tough Trenches Trophy

    d. Wild Hog Trophy

11. In which season did LSU have two defensive linemen named first-team All-Americans?

    a. 2005

    b. 2003

    c. 2004

    d. 2006

12. Who holds the LSU record for most sacks in a game?

    a. Lewis Neal

    b. Chuck Wiley

c. Arden Key

d. Gabe Northern

13. Who holds the LSU record for most sacks in a career?

a. Gabe Northern

b. Rydell Melancon

c. Ron Sancho

d. Marcus Spears

14. What is the LSU record for most tackles in a game?

a. 24

b. 23

c. 22

d. 21

15. Who is not one of the three players with at least five tackles for a loss in a single game?

a. Booger McFarland

b. Gabe Northern

c. Glenn Dorsey

d. Marcus Spears

16. Al Richardson holds the LSU record for tackles in a game and career tackles, but not single-season tackles.

a. True

b. False

17. What is Booger McFarland's real first name?

a. Allen

b. Adrian

c. Arthur

d. Anthony

18. The last time LSU held an opponent to zero or fewer rushing yards was in 2003 against South Carolina.

   a. True

   b. False

19. Which team did LSU sack nine times in 1994 to set the school record for sacks in a game?

   a. Arkansas

   b. Mississippi State

   c. Tulane

   d. Kentucky

20. Which award did Glenn Dorsey not win in 2007?

   a. Lombardi Award

   b. Outland Trophy

   c. Nagurski Award

   d. Bednarik Award

QUIZ ANSWERS

1. D – Marvin Stewart

2. A – Bill May

3. B – False

4. C – 1977

5. A – Roy Winston

6. A – True

7. D – Alan Faneca

8. C – Ben Wilkerson

9. C – Ethan Pocic

10. B – Joe Moore Award

11. A – 2005

12. B – Chuck Wiley

13. B – Rydell Melancon

14. D – 21

15. C – Glenn Dorsey

16. A – True

17. D – Anthony

18. B – False

19. C – Tulane

20. D – Bednarik Award

DID YOU KNOW?

1. Though Rudy Niswanger is likely not a name many LSU fans remember on the field, he might be the most decorated LSU player off the field during his time in Baton Rouge. As a senior in 2005, Niswanger was awarded the William V. Campbell Trophy, often referred to as the Academic Heisman, for his work in the classroom at LSU. In addition to graduating with a perfect 4.0 GPA, Niswanger scored a 33 on his MCAT, ranking in the top 8 percent of the country. He also was awarded the inaugural Wuerffel Trophy in 2005 at the "college football player who best combines exemplary community service with outstanding academic and athletic achievement."

2. Ben Wilkerson was one of the most dominant centers in college football in 2003 and 2004 as an anchor on the LSU offensive line. Wilkerson was a finalist for the Rimington Trophy in 2003, while leading the Tigers to the national championship, and then won the award the following year despite missing the final four games of the season with a knee injury. He was a first team All-American in 2004 and a second teamer in 2003 and was named to the All-SEC freshman team in 2001. LSU was 33-8 in the 41 games he started at center.

3. If not for a phone call, from an unnamed LSU assistant coach, Alan Faneca might have played for rival Alabama

and become an All-American in Tuscaloosa. The day before signing day in 1994, Faneca had made up his mind to go to Alabama and he then received a phone call from the assistant who was recruiting him. "He dropped a lot of four-letter words," Faneca told the media before his induction into the Louisiana Sports Hall of Fame. "I'd have to say he cursed me out. After I hung up the phone, I looked around my room and it was all purple and gold. ... I thought to myself, 'What am I doing? I'm screwing up.' I thought about it, woke up on signing day, and said I'm going to LSU." Tigers coach Curley Hallman was unaware that Faneca flipped in the last 24 hours because the assistant was too afraid to tell Hallman the bad news before Faneca changed his mind.

4. Kevin Mawae's football journey began in Germany, where his dad was stationed as a member of the U.S. Army. When Mawae was an 8-year-old playing flag football, his coach took the mental aspect of the game very seriously and Mawae credited that approach to helping him be inducted into the Pro Football Hall of Fame in 2019. In his enshrinement speech, Mawae detailed how coach Fred Moses helped prepare him for a life in football. Mawae said Moses would have the entire team sit in the dark movie theatre before games to envision success and run the plays through their mind. Those mental reps became a part of Mawae's pregame ritual for how to prepare for games.

5. LSU's offensive line won the 2019 Joe Moore Award, which has been given annually since 2015 to the most outstanding

offensive line unit in the country. The 2019 unit had only two linemen who started all 13 games at the same position before bowl season and eight different linemen started at least one game for the Tigers as they paved the way for the most impressive season of offense in school history. The voters all pointed to LSU's exception pass protection as the main reason why the unit won the award, crediting the Tigers for their physicality and patience while blocking for extended periods in the passing game.

6. Glenn Dorsey's development into an All-American defensive lineman was nothing short of a miracle in some respects. When Dorsey was 3 years old, it wasn't certain that he would ever be able to walk properly because he was bow-legged and pigeon-toed as a toddler. Doctors put him in heavy metal braces for a year and he came out of them ready to attack the world. He began playing football at 8 years old and became a dominant force in the Pop Warner leagues, leading to comparisons to the titular character in the movie *Forrest Gump*.

7. Most people probably know Anthony McFarland by his nickname, Booger, a pet name from his mother that just kind of stuck with him. His mom gave him the nickname when he was two and "a bad kid, getting into a lot of wild stuff." He was called many other things when he was younger, but Booger is the nickname that stuck and followed him throughout his career. Even when he thought he would be able to ditch the nickname when he arrived at LSU, the public address announcer boomed through Tiger Stadium,

"On the tackle for LSU, No. 94, Booger McFarland," after McFarland's first tackle as a freshman.

8. Marcus Spears made the biggest play of LSU's 2003 national championship victory over Oklahoma. After sacking Jason White on first down, Spears drifted into coverage on a zone blitz, intercepted White, and rumbled 20 yards into the end zone for what turned out to be the winning points in LSU's 21-14 victory. That play likely jumpstarted Spears into the 2004 season when he became a consensus All-American as a senior after forgoing the NFL draft.

9. Perhaps the greatest what-if story in recent memory at LSU was Arden Key, who set the school's single-season sacks record in 2016 as a sophomore. However, he missed spring practice the following year as he took a leave of absence from the team and he was not the same dominant force in 2017 after rejoining the team. Part of the reason is Key missed the beginning of the season was that he was recovering from shoulder surgery, but Key went from being a potential first-round pick to a third-round selection in the 2018 NFL draft.

10. Between his sophomore and junior seasons at LSU, Devin White bought a horse. A native of Cotton Valley, Louisiana, White saw a YouTube video in July 2018 about a mare for sale in Tennessee. He viewed the video twice before borrowing a friend's truck and heading to retrieve Daisy Mae, whom he bought with leftover money from his scholarship and stipends. White would occasionally ride

Daisy Mae along some trails around Baton Rouge during the season, and he said he felt at home in the more secluded parts of the city when he was on his horse.

CHAPTER 7:

NO AIR ZONE

QUIZ TIME!

1. The LSU team record for interceptions in a season is 25, set in 1953 and tied in 1970.

   a. True
   b. False

2. When was the last time LSU held an opponent to zero passing yards?

   a. 1949
   b. 1956
   c. 1963
   d. 1971

3. Who did LSU play in 1951 when it set the school record with eight interceptions?

   a. Tulane
   b. Maryland
   c. Villanova
   d. Southern Mississippi

4. Who did not return an interception for a touchdown on October 12, 1991, when LSU set a school record with three pick-sixes against Arkansas State?

   a. Carlton Buckels
   b. David Walkup
   c. Wayne Williams
   d. Corey Raymond

5. Who is not one of the seven players tied for the LSU record with three interceptions in a game?

   a. Cedric Donaldson
   b. Kenny Konz
   c. Clinton Burrell
   d. Craig Steltz

6. Who holds the NCAA record with 32 passes defended in a single season?

   a. Corey Webster
   b. Greedy Williams
   c. Tyrann Mathieu
   d. Patrick Peterson

7. How many fumbles did Tyrann Mathieu force during his LSU career to set the SEC record?

   a. 10
   b. 12
   c. 13
   d. 11

8. Both of LSU's 100-yard interception returns for a touchdown came against Mississippi State.

   a. True

   b. False

9. Which of these LSU defensive backs did not win the Thorpe Award?

   a. Patrick Peterson

   b. Morris Claiborne

   c. Tyrann Mathieu

   d. Grant Delpit

10. In which place did Tyrann Mathieu finish in the 2011 Heisman Trophy voting?

    a. 4th

    b. 5th

    c. 6th

    d. 7th

11. How many first-team All-American defensive backs has LSU had?

    a. 13

    b. 15

    c. 17

    d. 19

12. Which of these safeties was not a consensus first-team All-American?

    a. LaRon Landry

    b. Craig Steltz

c. Eric Reid

d. Jamal Adams

13. In which season did Craig Burns set the single-season interception record at LSU?

    a. 1973

    b. 1972

    c. 1971

    d. 1970

14. Chris Williams is the only player in school history with 20 career interceptions.

    a. True

    b. False

15. LaRon Landry is the only non-offensive lineman in the top four in consecutive starts. How many straight games did Landry start to end his LSU career?

    a. 47

    b. 48

    c. 49

    d. 50

16. The 2003 LSU defense set the school record with seven defensive touchdowns. Who was the only defender to reach the end zone twice that season?

    a. Corey Webster

    b. Travis Daniels

    c. Lionel Turner

    d. Jack Hunt

17. What is Greedy Williams' legal first name?

    a. Andraez
    b. Antoine
    c. Greedy
    d. Charles

18. How did Morris Claiborne cap off LSU's win over Georgia in the 2011 SEC Championship game?

    a. 45-yard interception return for a touchdown
    b. 67-yard punt return for a touchdown
    c. 99-yard kickoff return for a touchdown
    d. 27-yard fumble return for a touchdown

19. Which award did Patrick Peterson not win during his historic 2010 season in Baton Rouge?

    a. SEC Special Teams Player of the Year
    b. Bednarik Award
    c. Nagurski Award
    d. SEC Defensive Player of the Year

20. Tommy Casanova was a consensus All-American all three years he was a first-team selection.

    a. True
    b. False

QUIZ ANSWERS

1. B – False

2. D – 1971

3. C – Villanova

4. C – Wayne Williams

5. A – Cedric Donaldson

6. A – Corey Webster

7. D – 11

8. A – True

9. C – Tyrann Mathieu

10. B – 5th

11. C – 17

12. D – Jamal Adams

13. D – 1970

14. A – True

15. B – 48

16. D – Jack Hunt

17. A – Andraez

18. A – 45-yard interception return for a touchdown

19. C – Nagurski Award

20. B – False

DID YOU KNOW?

1. Tommy Casanova was the only LSU player named to the Walter Camp All-Century team in 1999, among the 82 honored. Casanova intercepted seven passes in his career, that included him being a first-team All-American at cornerback from 1969 through 1971. He played in all three phases during his time at LSU but was mostly a cornerback. His coach, Charles McClendon, said Casanova was "one of the most gifted athletes I ever coached. There's no question in my mind he could've been an All-American running back. He could really have jazzed up our offense."

2. Casanova and Craig Burns combined to almost single-handedly take down Mississippi in 1970 for the Tigers' only SEC title under coach Charles McClendon. In the 61-17 rout of the Rebels at Tiger Stadium, Casanova had an interception and returned two punts for touchdowns, while Burns returned a punt for a touchdown, in addition to his three interceptions. It is still the most lopsided game in the series' history, and it propelled LSU to the Orange Bowl that season against Nebraska.

3. Chris Williams holds at least a piece of every LSU interceptions record. He is one of seven players to intercept three passes in a game, doing so against Rice in 1978. That same year, he intercepted eight passes, tying Burns' 1970 season for the top spot in the record book. Over his four

years in Baton Rouge, Williams had 20 interceptions, four more than Corey Webster, who ranks second in Tigers' history. Williams was a first team All-SEC selection in 1978 and 1980, and a second-team selection in 1979.

4. Corey Webster was a high school quarterback who signed at LSU thinking he would play wide receiver on the gridiron for the Tigers, and also compete on the basketball court in Baton Rouge. Webster never made it onto the court for the Tigers, but he did excel on the football field, albeit on the opposite side of the ball. Webster caught seven passes as a freshman before converting to cornerback for his final three seasons. He led the SEC with seven interceptions as a sophomore then was an All-American at cornerback in his final two seasons in Baton Rouge.

5. LaRon Landry made an early impact at LSU by leading the 2003 national championship team in tackles with 80. He started 10 games that season and was an integral member of the Tigers' first national championship in 45 seasons. However, when Landry reflected back on that season as he entered his senior year in Baton Rouge, he told reporters, "I had tunnel vision. I really didn't worry about the crowd, what everybody else's assignment was. I just played ball. I really didn't have that mental aspect of the game. I would just guard [the receiver]. It was a physical thing, playing, creating havoc. ... It's very funny when I look back on it."

6. Patrick Peterson became the first LSU defender to win the Chuck Bednarik Award in 2010 and he was also the first

player ever to be named both SEC Defensive Player of the Year and SEC Special Teams Player of the Year that season. Peterson had four interceptions and broke up six other passes but made his biggest impact as a returner. The cornerback set the school record for kick return yardage and led the SEC in both kick return and punt return yardage. He returned two punts for touchdowns that season as well to add to his case.

7. Morris Claiborne came to LSU as an athlete and floated between the offense and defense as a receiver and cornerback. One day, a graduate assistant gave Claiborne a piece of advice that would change the trajectory of his career. The assistant told him that receivers like Claiborne were far easier to find than corners like him. Claiborne decided to stay on defense and, after talking with coach Les Miles, the coach agreed that Claiborne should stay on defense. Two years later, he won the Jim Thorpe Award as the best defensive back in college football.

8. Tyrann Mathieu was awarded the Bednarik as the best defensive player in college football in 2011, and finished fifth in the Heisman voting, but it was Claiborne who won the Thorpe Award that season. He had 76 tackles, forced six fumbles, intercepted two passes, and was credited with nine pass breakups in 2011, in addition to returning two punts for a touchdown. It was a worthwhile risk for LSU, which hadn't shown any interest in Mathieu until late in the recruiting cycle after missing out on other cornerback prospects. Until LSU's offer came, only Florida International,

Miami (Ohio), Louisiana-Monroe, and Tulane had offered the cornerback.

9. Eric Reid was born to compete in some sport at LSU. His father, Eric Reid Sr., won a national championship in the 110-meter hurdles at the school and still worked there when the younger Reid was making his college decision. There are pictures of Reid from as young as 7 years of age wearing a full LSU uniform complete with plastic helmet and he grew up loving the school his father attended. Of course, his parents forced him to take all five of his permitted official visits despite his early commitment to LSU, and really challenged him about his desire to play at LSU.

10. Grant Delpit's decision to sign with LSU was a homecoming of sorts for the 2019 Jim Thorpe Award winner. Delpit lived in New Orleans for the first six years of his life before his family was displaced by Hurricane Katrina. The week before the storm hit, Delpit was the first pick in his youth football league draft as a 6-year-old. He learned to field punts on the golf course behind his house in New Orleans and was excited to play tackle football that first year he was allowed. However, his family ended up moving to Houston after Katrina hit when they saw their house flooded on television from what they thought was going to be a temporary trip to Memphis to wait out the storm.

CHAPTER 8:

COACHING CAROUSEL

QUIZ TIME!

1. Who was the first coach to win the national championship at LSU?

    a. Charles McClendon
    b. Bernie Moore
    c. Paul Dietzel
    d. Nick Saban

2. Who is the only coach since 1934 to not lead LSU to a bowl game in his tenure?

    a. Mike Archer
    b. Curley Hallman
    c. Jerry Stovall
    d. Gus Tinsley

3. Who was the interim coach in 1999 who led LSU to a win over Arkansas after Gerry DiNardo was fired?

    a. Nick Saban
    b. Hal Hunter

c. Charlie Coiner

d. Lou Tepper

4. Gerry DiNardo had a winning record as LSU's coach.

    a. True

    b. False

5. How many wins did Charles McClendon have at LSU to set the program record for coaching wins?

    a. 121

    b. 128

    c. 132

    d. 137

6. Who was the first LSU graduate to coach the Tigers?

    a. Edmond Chavanne

    b. John Mayhew

    c. Gus Tinsley

    d. Jerry Stovall

7. Which future Power Five coach did not spend at least one season as an assistant at LSU?

    a. Bo Pelini

    b. Mack Brown

    c. Jimbo Fisher

    d. Kevin Sumlin

8. How much was Albert Simmonds paid by LSU to coach the 1894 and 1895 seasons?

    a. $100

    b. $200

c. $300

d. $400

9. LSU has never had a coach who played at a different SEC school.

   a. True

   b. False

10. How many coaches did LSU have between 1893 and 1934?

    a. 14

    b. 15

    c. 17

    d. 19

11. Which LSU coach was not previously an assistant coach at LSU before becoming head coach?

    a. Paul Dietzel

    b. Jerry Stovall

    c. Charles McClendon

    d. Mike Archer

12. What was the only season in which LSU had a losing record under Charles McClendon?

    a. 1966

    b. 1974

    c. 1975

    d. 1976

13. For how many days was Bo Rein the coach at LSU before being killed in a plane crash?

a. 21

b. 28

c. 35

d. 42

14. before Curley Hallman's tenure, who was the last coach to leave LSU with a losing record in his career with the Tigers?

a. Wayne Sutton

b. Jerry Stovall

c. Gus Tinsley

d. Russ Cohen

15. The only four LSU coaches to be named the national coach of the year were those who won LSU's national championships.

a. True

b. False

16. What other sport did Bernie Moore coach at LSU before being named the Tigers' football coach?

a. Swimming

b. Track & Field

c. Basketball

d. Baseball

17. Which bowl game proved to be Nick Saban's last game as LSU's head coach?

a. Outback Bowl

b. Peach Bowl

c. Capital One Bowl

d. Sugar Bowl

18. From which school did LSU hire Les Milles to replace Nick Saban?

    a. Arkansas State
    b. Texas Tech
    c. Oklahoma State
    d. Louisiana Tech

19. Which position group did Ed Orgeron coach in 2015-16 before getting promoted to interim head coach?

    a. Running Backs
    b. Linebackers
    c. Offensive Line
    d. Defensive Line

20. The last three LSU coaches have all had winning percentages of at least .750 with the Tigers.

    a. True
    b. False

QUIZ ANSWERS

1. C – Paul Dietzel

2. B – Curley Hallman

3. B – Hal Hunter

4. A – True

5. D – 137

6. A – Edmond Chavanne

7. D – Kevin Sumlin

8. C – $300

9. B – False

10. D – 19

11. A – Paul Dietzel

12. C – 1975

13. D – 42

14. A – Wayne Sutton

15. B – False

16. B – Track & Field

17. C – Capital One Bowl

18. C – Oklahoma State

19. D – Defensive Line

20. A – True

DID YOU KNOW?

1. LSU's second coach was the first one to get paid for coaching. After realizing that coaching might not be the best option for the team, Charles Coates decided to pay Albert Simmons $300 to coach the team in 1894 and 1895. LSU won five of the six games it played under Simmons.

2. Bernie Moore did a lot for LSU and the SEC as a whole during his career in college athletics. He began his career in Baton Rouge as the Tigers' track and field coach, leading LSU to its first national title in 1933. He took over the football program in 1935 and immediately won two SEC titles with the Tigers, in 1935 and 1936. He won 83 games over 13 seasons at the helm of LSU's football program and then went on to be the longest-serving commissioner in the SEC, holding the position from 1948 through 1965.

3. Paul Dietzel revolutionized college football with his three-team system, designed to deal with the substitution rules in place in his era. A new rule meant that players could only return to the field once each quarter after being substituted off, so Dietzel came up with three different units in 1958. He had his 11 best players on the first team, his next best 11 offensive players on the second team, and his 11 next best defensive players on a third team. That system helped the Tigers win the national championship in 1958 and boosted Dietzel to national prominence as the youngest coach to be

named coach of the year. Dietzel returned to LSU as athletics director for four years from 1978 to 82.

4. Charles McClendon is the longest-tenured and winningest coach in LSU history, with 137 wins over 18 years with the Tigers that featured just one losing season. He began his coaching career as an assistant at Kentucky to Bear Bryant, who had coached him during his college football days. He then came to LSU as an assistant to Dietzel, including on the 1958 national championship team. He coached 17 All-Americans while at LSU and was twice named the national coach of the year. Despite his success with the Tigers, McClendon was forced out because of his 2-14 record against Bryant's Alabama squads and the lack of national championships.

5. Bo Rein tragically died after just 42 days on the job as LSU's coach. He was an innovative offensive mind who was hired to replace McClendon. Rein was flying home from a recruiting trip in Shreveport, when the private plane he was on crashed into the Atlantic Ocean. The coach was en route back to Baton Rouge, a flight of less than an hour, when storms caused the pilot to try to detour to Memphis. The approval of the re-route was the last contact with the pilot and the plane continued to fly until crashing off the Virginia coast. It is unclear what happened in the cockpit, as the Coast Guard plane sent to contact the plane was never able to communicate with the cockpit as it followed the plane until its crash.

6. Jerry Stovall was the emergency choice to take over the program after Rein's death. Stovall, in addition to being a star on the field for the Tigers, had worked as LSU's running backs coach under McClendon from 1974-78. He had taken a fundraising position in the LSU athletics department in 1979 before being thrust into the spotlight. It was a mixed bag of results on the field for Stovall, though he did end LSU's 11-game losing streak to Alabama in 1982 with a 20-10 win that helped boost the Tigers to play in the Orange Bowl that season.

7. Gerry DiNardo inherited the LSU coaching job at one of the program's down points after six consecutive losing seasons. The first three seasons under DiNardo were a success, as the Tigers had a winning record in all three seasons and won a share of the SEC West crown in 1996 and 1997. However, DiNardo is still upset at himself for how the team performed in 1998 and 1999, which ultimately led to his dismissal. He had plenty of special moments at LSU, but he said in an interview before the 2020 season, "Yeah, you know I wish I had done a better job there. I think LSU, I think of the last two years. I don't think about the white jerseys. I don't think about the three bowl games. I don't think about beating Florida. I think about the last two years. I wish I had done better. And so, when that's your perspective, then when you watch them, you know what the potential was, and I didn't reach it. And it makes it hard. I wish I had been better."

8. Nick Saban was not on the original list of candidates for the LSU job after the Tigers fired DiNardo in 1999. Saban actually

instructed his agent, Jimmy Sexton, to make contact with LSU athletics director Joe Dean about the position, and the talks escalated from there. Saban wanted a new football administration building as well as more resources and a separate academic center for the student-athletes. Mark Emmert, who was LSU's chancellor at the time, agreed to the conditions and four years later, Saban delivered the school its first national championship since 1958. Four of Saban's assistants during his stint at LSU became head coaches in the SEC, one became the head coach at another Power Five school and a sixth, Freddie Kitchens, coached the Cleveland Browns for a season.

9. Les Miles had plenty of quirks during his time at LSU, as he became just the second coach to win 100 games with the Tigers. What most people know about Miles is his appetite for the grass at Tiger Stadium, which he said tasted the best. Miles began his grass-eating habit as a right fielder on his Little League team, but it rose to prominence in 2010 when he was spotted munching on a blade during LSU's game against Alabama. The legend of the "Mad Hatter" only accelerated from there as his grass-eating became as large a part of his character as the wins he accumulated at LSU.

10. Ed Orgeron's energy is infectious, and it has helped him enter many doors as a college coach. He was hired as an assistant strength and conditioning coach at Arkansas because of his enthusiasm, and it was the same reason Jimmy Johnson hired him to coach at Miami. But expending all that energy means Orgeron works up quite an appetite,

which is where the recruiting stories come in. It seems like every LSU player has a different story about a meal they had with Orgeron when he was recruiting them, from gumbo at Grant Delpit's house to bison chili at offensive lineman Austin Deculus' home, and even the famous crawfish story with Joe Burrow where Orgeron ordered crawfish to a restaurant that didn't serve it in order to give Burrow a southern experience.

CHAPTER 9:

CHAMPIONSHIP CALIBER

QUIZ TIME!

1. What was NOT the name of one of Paul Dietzel's platoons during the 1958 championship season?

   a. Gold Team
   b. White Team
   c. Black Team
   d. Chinese Bandits

2. Which team did LSU NOT shut out during its perfect run through the 1958 season?

   a. Tulane
   b. Alabama
   c. Miami
   d. Mississippi

3. Who was the only team to trip up LSU on its way to the 2003 national title?

   a. Auburn
   b. Mississippi

c. Georgia

d. Florida

4. LSU never allowed more than 20 points in a game during the 2003 season.

   a. True

   b. False

5. With which school did LSU officially share the 2003 national championship because the Associated Press did not vote the Tigers No. 1 at the end of the season?

   a. Southern California

   b. Ohio State

   c. Texas

   d. Oklahoma

6. Who was named the Most Valuable Player of the 2003 national championship game?

   a. Marcus Spears

   b. Matt Mauck

   c. Michael Clayton

   d. Justin Vincent

7. Which future FBS head coach was not on LSU's staff during the 2003 season?

   a. Jimbo Fisher

   b. Derek Dooley

   c. Kirby Smart

   d. Will Muschamp

8. How many ranked opponents did LSU face during the 2007 regular season?

   a. 4
   b. 5
   c. 6
   d. 7

9. LSU was No. 1 in the country for both of its losses during the 2007 season.

   a. True
   b. False

10. Who did not score a touchdown during LSU's 31-0 run after Ohio State took a 10-0 lead in the 2007 national championship game?

    a. Brandon LaFell
    b. Early Doucet
    c. Jacob Hester
    d. Demetrius Byrd

11. Who returned an interception for a touchdown to beat Tennessee in the SEC Championship game in 2007 and propel LSU into the national championship game?

    a. Chevis Jackson
    b. Jonathan Zenon
    c. Ali Highsmith
    d. Craig Steltz

12. Who was credited with the blocked field goal in the 2007 national championship game?

a. Ricky Jean-Francois
b. Tyson Jackson
c. Darry Beckwith
d. Ron Brooks

13. What was the score of the regular season game between LSU and Alabama in 2011?

a. 3-0
b. 6-3
c. 9-6
d. 10-6

14. Which of the following LSU opponents during the 2011 regular season did not finish in the top five of the final Associated Press poll?

a. Alabama
b. Oregon
c. Arkansas
d. West Virginia

15. The 2011 LSU team set the school record for most double-digit victories.

a. True
b. False

16. How many touchdowns did the 2019 squad score during its run to a national championship?

a. 93
b. 95
c. 97
d. 99

17. LSU gained more than 100 yards more per game in 2019 than its second-most yards per game in program history.

    a. True
    b. False

18. Which city hosted the 2019 College Football Playoff national championship game between LSU and Clemson?

    a. Pasadena
    b. Phoenix
    c. Atlanta
    d. New Orleans

19. Who scored the touchdown that gave LSU the lead for the first time against Clemson in the 2019 national title game?

    a. Thaddeus Moss
    b. Ja'Marr Chase
    c. Clyde Edwards-Helaire
    d. Justin Jefferson

20. Who was the defensive MVP of the 2019 national championship game?

    a. Grant Delpit
    b. Kristian Fulton
    c. Patrick Queen
    d. JaCoby Stevens

QUIZ ANSWERS

1. C – Black Team

2. B – Alabama

3. D – Florida

4. B – False

5. A – Southern California

6. D – Justin Vincent

7. C – Kirby Smart

8. C – 6

9. A – True

10. D – Demetrius Byrd

11. B – Jonathan Zenon

12. A – Ricky Jean-Francois

13. C – 9-6

14. D – West Virginia

15. A – True

16. B – 95

17. A – True

18. D – New Orleans

19. B – Ja'Marr Chase

20. C – Patrick Queen

DID YOU KNOW?

1. Every national championship game played in New Orleans since 1999 has featured LSU. The Tigers won the 2003, 2007, and 2019 national titles at the Superdome and lost the 2011 title game to Alabama in New Orleans. Even the 1958 national championship season culminated in a win in the Sugar Bowl in New Orleans.

2. It's a nickname that definitely wouldn't fly in modern-day society, but the LSU players and fans rallied around the Chinese Bandits nickname for the Tigers' all-defensive lineup in 1958. Paul Dietzel nicknamed the group the Chinese Bandits after reading a comic strip called "Terry and The Pirates", where a character said that Chinese bandits were the most vicious people in the world. The players were emboldened by their success on the field and fans began wearing Chinese straw hats to games, which were provided by a local restaurateur.

3. LSU had already clinched the 1958 national championship by the time it played in the Sugar Bowl, but the Tigers had a chance to complete an unblemished season against Clemson. The Tigers won the game 7-0 with a few pieces of good luck in the third quarter. Clemson's long snapper bounced the snap to the punter and LSU fell on the ball at the 11-yard line. On third down, LSU called a halfback pass and Billy Cannon rolled to his right as he was looking for a receiver.

The play was designed to go to Johnny Robinson, but Clemson had him covered, so Cannon threw it to Mickey Mangham, who made the catch for the touchdown. Cannon has called it "a pass the Lord threw" because of how unsure he was about whether or not it would work.

4. Some may argue a broken thumb in 2000 saved the 2003 national championship team. In training camp before the 2000 season, coach Nick Saban asked Matt Mauck to switch to safety, thinking the quarterback would have a better future on the other side of the ball. Mauck asked for one more week of practice at quarterback and Craig Nall unfortunately broke his thumb while holding a field goal attempt. Mauck stayed on as the third quarterback and rallied LSU in the 2001 SEC Championship game before guiding the Tigers to the 2003 national title with a then-school record 28 touchdown passes.

5. The 2003 national title still stirs up some mixed feelings among college football fans. It is the last national championship to be split between two teams officially, as LSU won the BCS title game over Oklahoma and was voted No. 1 in the *USA Today* Coaches' Poll, while Southern California was voted No. 1 by the Associated Press after beating Michigan in the Rose Bowl. There was even controversy about who should play in the official BCS title game because USC and LSU were Nos. 1 and 2 in both human polls, with Oklahoma at No. 3 after getting shellacked in the Big 12 title game for its first loss of the season. Yet the computers liked the Sooners too much, and

the Tigers were able to make up enough ground in strength of schedule to nip the Trojans for the second spot.

6. One of Les Miles' rallying cry to the media during the 2007 season was that his Tigers were undefeated in regulation. Indeed, LSU's only two losses in a wacky college football season were in triple overtime to Kentucky and triple overtime to Arkansas. In the week leading up to the SEC Championship game against Tennessee, and again after beating the Volunteers, Miles made that simple argument for why his team should play for the national title. Miles actually stole the "undefeated in regulation" line from his wife, Kathy, who was just trying to cheer up her husband after the loss to the Razorbacks. Instead, it might have been the exact argument Miles needed to politic his team to the 2007 national title.

7. By winning the title in 2007, LSU set a pair of interesting records. The Tigers became the first school to win two BCS national championships and the first team since Minnesota in 1960 to win a national title with two losses.

8. The loss in the 2011 national title game was particularly tough for LSU because it lost to rival Alabama and former coach Nick Saban. The Tigers were the only unbeaten team in the country after the conference championship games and were given a rematch with Alabama for the national championship. LSU won an epic 9-6 slugfest in Tuscaloosa during the regular season but was shut out 21-0 in the title game. However, LSU finished that season with wins over

three of the other four teams in the top five of the final Associated Press poll.

9. In the 2019 College Football Playoff semifinal against Oklahoma, Ja'Marr Chase received the only handoff of his career. It was caused by a coaching mistake, one Chase corrected by stepping next to Joe Burrow and taking the handoff. LSU was in Oklahoma's red zone and running an up-tempo offense with four receivers and a tight end on the field when facing fourth-and-two. The coaches signaled in a running play to try to extend the drive, but there was no running back on the field. Chase realized the problem, calmly took his spot in the backfield, and carried for 5 yards and the first down.

10. The championship rings the 2019 team received had a special tieback to the first LSU national championship team. The rings were made by Warren Rabb, who was the quarterback on the 1958 national championship squad and now owns a Jostens franchise in Baton Rouge. Rabb got into the ring business after receiving a call at one in the morning from a recruiter who was looking for someone to work a sales job in Louisiana. Rabb said he still wears his championship ring every day and, though it isn't as gaudy as the modern rings, he still thinks it's the prettiest ring in the world.

CHAPTER 10:

GOING BOWLING

QUIZ TIME!

1. How many consecutive seasons did LSU play in a bowl game before the 2020 season, when the streak ended?

   a. 23
   b. 22
   c. 21
   d. 20

2. Which bowl game was the first LSU played in that wasn't the Sugar Bowl?

   a. Peach
   b. Cotton
   c. Orange
   d. Sun

3. Who did LSU play in the 1947 Cotton Bowl, affectionately known as the "Ice Bowl"?

   a. Texas Christian
   b. Arkansas

c. Texas

d. Oklahoma

4. Who did LSU beat for its first win in a bowl game?

    a. Texas A&M

    b. Santa Clara

    c. Oklahoma

    d. Arkansas

5. LSU has an unbeaten record in multiple appearances in which bowl game?

    a. Outback

    b. Fiesta

    c. Gator

    d. Independence

6. LSU has a losing record in the Sugar Bowl.

    a. True

    b. False

7. Which of these opponents has LSU never played in a bowl game?

    a. Baylor

    b. Stanford

    c. Wake Forest

    d. Oklahoma State

8. Which team has not shut out LSU in a bowl game?

    a. Mississippi

    b. Santa Clara

c. Texas

d. Oklahoma

9. LSU has played in all six bowl games that are now part of the College Football Playoff rotation.

   a. True

   b. False

10. Who has not returned a kick or punt for a touchdown in an LSU bowl game?

    a. Tyrann Mathieu

    b. Craig Burns

    c. Leonard Fournette

    d. Eddie Kennison

11. Who caught the only touchdown in LSU's win over Clemson in the 1959 Sugar Bowl to complete the 1958 championship season?

    a. Billy Hendrix

    b. Mickey Mangham

    c. Don Norwood

    d. Johnny Robinson

12. Who recovered a blocked punt for a touchdown against Colorado in the 1962 Orange Bowl?

    a. Gene Sykes

    b. Bo Campbell

    c. Earl Gros

    d. Roy Winston

13. How many interceptions did Jeff Wickersham throw in the 1985 Sugar Bowl loss to Nebraska?

    a. 3
    b. 6
    c. 4
    d. 5

14. Against whom did Kevin Faulk rush for 234 yards to set the LSU postseason record in the 1995 Independence Bowl?

    a. Oklahoma State
    b. Notre Dame
    c. Michigan State
    d. Florida State

15. Josh Reed set LSU's postseason record for TD catches in the 2002 Sugar Bowl win over Illinois.

    a. True
    b. False

16. Who was on the other end of the biggest bowl win for LSU in the 2005 Peach Bowl?

    a. Texas A&M
    b. Notre Dame
    c. Miami
    d. Clemson

17. Which team handed Les Miles his first non-conference loss at LSU in the 2010 Capital One Bowl?

    a. Notre Dame
    b. Penn State

c. Iowa

d. Wisconsin

18. Leonard Fournette set an NCAA record with his five total touchdowns in the 2015 Texas Bowl against Texas Tech.

a. True

b. False

19. LSU has won five of its last six postseason appearances. Which team is the only one to defeat the Tigers in a bowl game during that stretch?

a. Texas Tech

b. Louisville

c. Iowa

d. Notre Dame

20. What record did LSU not break during the 2019 Peach Bowl rout of Oklahoma?

a. Passing yards

b. Total yards

c. First downs

d. Combined points

QUIZ ANSWERS

1. D – 20

2. C – Orange

3. B – Arkansas

4. A – Texas A&M

5. D – Independence

6. A – True

7. D – Oklahoma State

8. C – Texas

9. B – False

10. A – Tyrann Mathieu

11. B – Mickey Mangham

12. A – Gene Sykes

13. D – 5

14. C – Michigan State

15. B – False

16. C – Miami

17. B – Penn State

18. A – True

19. D – Notre Dame

20. C – First Downs

DID YOU KNOW?

1. During the recent 20-year bowl streak, LSU went 14-7 in 21 bowl appearances, with two of those wins coming en route to the 2019 national championship. The stretch accounts for half of LSU's 28 bowl victories, which ranks eighth nationally and fourth in the SEC. LSU's first bowl win was a 19-14 victory in the 1944 Orange Bowl against Texas A&M.

2. LSU went to the Sugar Bowl three straight years, from 1936 through 1938, and lost all three games. In 1936, the Tigers were tripped up 3-2 by TCU in the first bowl game without a touchdown. The two teams combined for just 15 first downs as four days of rain showers made the field too waterlogged for the offense to succeed. The following season, LSU was upset by Santa Clara 21-14, ruining the school's perfect season. The Broncos came back to New Orleans in 1938 and shut out the Tigers with a pair of late goal-line stands to preserve the victory.

3. Perhaps no non-championship bowl game is more famous in LSU lore than the 1947 Cotton Bowl, nicknamed the Ice Bowl. The snow and sleet that blanketed Dallas the day of the game made conditions slippery, but LSU handled the adverse weather well against Arkansas. The Tigers used oil drums as makeshift heaters by lighting charcoal in them, and the fans even made some fires in the stands to keep warm. LSU held a 271-54 advantage in yards and a 15-1 edge

in first downs, but it could not break through for any points against the stingy Razorbacks. The game ended in a 0-0 tie, the only tie in LSU's bowl history.

4. The other most famous game from the pre-SEC era of the LSU-Arkansas rivalry came in the 1966 Cotton Bowl when the Tigers ended the Razorbacks' 22-game winning streak with a stunning 14-7 win. Arkansas entered the game at No. 2 in the nation and had the best offense in the country, averaging more than 32 points per game. Yet the Razorbacks were held scoreless after their opening drive and the defending national champions made two costly miscues – a fumble and poor kick – that set up the Tigers in excellent field position to score twice for the victory.

5. Kevin Faulk finished three yards short of the LSU record for rushing yards in a game with 234 yards and two touchdowns in the Tigers' win in the 1995 Independence Bowl. Faulk ran the ball just 25 times in the contest to set the yardage standard for LSU running backs in a bowl game. He was far from the only person who made big plays, though, as Gabe Northern returned a fumble for a touchdown and Eddie Kennison returned a kickoff 92 yards for a score. The Kennison touchdown was the first kickoff return score in LSU's bowl history and the third kick the Tigers had ever returned for a touchdown in a bowl game.

6. The 2000 Peach Bowl was vital in restoring the LSU football program to its current heights. It was Nick Saban's first year as the Tigers coach and he personally lobbied the president of the Peach Bowl for a spot in the game. Saban and chancellor

Mark Emmert met with the Peach Bowl president, and the Tigers ended up getting invited to the game, which was being broadcast unopposed on ESPN. The game was played in Atlanta, a recruiting hotbed. Rohan Davey orchestrated a second-half comeback to lead LSU to a 28-14 win over Georgia Tech and Saban later recalled that most of the recruits who signed with the Tigers that offseason watched that game and were sold on the program based on that performance.

7. Before Joe Burrow and Justin Jefferson torched Oklahoma in the 2019 Peach Bowl, another quarterback-receiver combo was ready to shine in a primetime bowl game. Rohan Davey and Josh Reed rewrote the LSU record book in the 2002 Sugar Bowl with stellar performances. Davey became the first LSU quarterback to throw for 400 yards in a postseason game by passing for 444 yards against Illinois and he still holds the bowl game record with 31 completions and 53 attempts against the Fighting Illini. His favorite target was Josh Reed, who caught 14 passes for 239 yards, which is also still atop the LSU record book for bowl performances. Not to be outshone, Domanick Davis ran for four touchdowns in the game, which stands as the LSU record to this day.

8. The most lopsided bowl game in LSU's history was the 2005 Peach Bowl against No. 9 Miami. The 10th ranked Tigers surrendered a field goal to open the game, and tied the contest with a field goal of their own late in the first quarter. That began a streak of eight straight scoring drives for LSU as the Tigers proceeded to score 37 straight points over the final three quarters for the victory over the Hurricanes. LSU

limited Miami to 153 yards in the game and held a 26-6 edge in first downs while only having to punt once in the entire game.

9. A year after setting several records in the Music City Bowl, Leonard Fournette owned the 2015 Texas Bowl for LSU. The sophomore running back tied an NCAA record with five touchdowns, including four on the ground, as he became the fourth LSU running back to exceed 200 rushing yards in a bowl game. He helped LSU set seven postseason records for the school as a team, including the 337 rushing yards and 9.7 yards per carry average records that still stand. The Tigers also set records by scoring 56 points in the win over Texas Tech, including a record 35 in the second half, and putting up 638 yards of total offense.

10. LSU's 2019 Peach Bowl performance broke many of the records LSU set in 2015. As a team, the Tigers set the school's postseason record for most points in a quarter (28 in the second), most points in a half (49 in the first), and most points in a game (63), as well as the most yards gained in a game (692). Jefferson's records were covered in Chapter 5 and Burrow set the world on fire with his performance that night against Oklahoma. Burrow set LSU postseason records for most touchdown passes in a game with seven, most passing yards in a game with 493, and best completion percentage with a minimum of 20 attempts at 74.4 percent. Burrow added to his resume in the national title game with 463 passing yards and five touchdowns, both totals that rank second in LSU history.

CHAPTER 11:

DRAFT DAY

QUIZ TIME!

1. Who is not one of the three LSU players to have been drafted No. 1 overall in the NFL?

   a. Joe Burrow
   b. Billy Cannon
   c. JaMarcus Russell
   d. Jerry Stovall

2. LSU has had a player chosen in every draft since the 1967 AFL-NFL merger.

   a. True
   b. False

3. Which one was the first Tigers player to be drafted by an NFL team?

   a. Abe Mickal
   b. Ken Kavanaugh
   c. Gus Tinsley
   d. Marvin Stewart

4. Steve Van Buren was the first LSU player to be a first-round draft pick. Which team selected him with the fifth overall selection?

   a. New York Giants
   b. Chicago Bears
   c. Philadelphia Eagles
   d. Green Bay Packers

5. With which pick did San Francisco select Y.A. Tittle when the quarterback re-entered the draft in 1951?

   a. 2nd
   b. 3rd
   c. 4th
   d. 5th

6. Which two teams drafted Billy Cannon in 1960 after his Heisman Trophy-winning season?

   a. New York Giants & Houston Oilers
   b. Los Angeles Rams & Houston Oilers
   c. New York Giants & Dallas Texans
   d. Los Angeles Rams & Dallas Texans

7. Who was the first LSU player to be a first-round draft pick after the AFL-NFL merger in 1967?

   a. Tommy Casanova
   b. Mike Williams
   c. John Garlington
   d. Bert Jones

8. Which LSU player did the New Orleans Saints select in the expansion draft?

   a. George Rice
   b. Bob Richards
   c. Jerry Stovall
   d. Earl Leggett

9. LSU had as many first-round picks in the 1960s as it had in the 1970s and 1980s combined.

   a. True
   b. False

10. In which round did Miami draft David Woodley before he led them to Super Bowl XVII?

   a. 8th
   b. 7th
   c. 9th
   d. 6th

11. The first former LSU player to win a Super Bowl went undrafted.

   a. True
   b. False

12. Who was not one of the first-round picks during LSU's longest streak with a first-round pick, from 2004 to 2009?

   a. Andrew Whitworth
   b. Michael Clayton
   c. Tyson Jackson
   d. Joseph Addai

13. Which of these players was not drafted by the New Orleans Saints?

    a. Al Woods
    b. Will Clapp
    c. Skyler Green
    d. Devery Henderson

14. Which of these LSU standouts was not a top-10 pick in the NFL draft?

    a. LaRon Landry
    b. Patrick Peterson
    c. Jamal Adams
    d. Odell Beckham Jr.

15. Who was not one of the five LSU players drafted in the first round of the 2020 NFL draft?

    a. Patrick Queen
    b. Clyde Edwards-Helaire
    c. K'Lavon Chaisson
    d. Grant Delpit

16. Before five LSU players were drafted in the first round in 2020, which draft featured the most LSU first-round picks with four?

    a. 2004
    b. 2007
    c. 2012
    d. 2017

17. LSU had more players drafted between 2006 and 2020 than Alabama.

    a. True
    b. False

18. How many first-round draft picks have come from LSU had since the merger in 1967?

    a. 39
    b. 37
    c. 35
    d. 33

19. How many LSU defensive backs were drafted between 2007 and 2020, leading the nation?

    a. 14
    b. 16
    c. 18
    d. 20

20. LSU tied the record for most players from one school drafted in a seven-round NFL draft in 2020. How many Tigers heard their name called that year?

    a. 12
    b. 13
    c. 14
    d. 15

QUIZ ANSWERS

1. D – Jerry Stovall

2. B – False

3. A – Abe Mickal

4. C – Philadelphia Eagles

5. B – 3rd

6. B – Los Angeles Rams & Houston Oilers

7. D – Bert Jones

8. D – Earl Leggett

9. A – True

10. A – 8th

11. B – False

12. A – Andrew Whitworth

13. C – Skyler Green

14. D – Odell Beckham Jr.

15. D – Grant Delpit

16. B – 2007

17. B – False

18. C – 35

19. D – 20

20. C – 14

DID YOU KNOW?

1. Billy Cannon was the subject of a lawsuit after the 1960 draft as part of a war between the NFL and AFL. Cannon was the first overall pick in the NFL draft by the Los Angeles Rams and the Houston Oilers chose Cannon in the AFL draft. The two teams then battled to sign Cannon, with the Rams agreeing to a three-year contract worth $15,000 per year plus a $10,000 signing bonus, that would start after LSU's bowl game. The Oilers had been unable to reach Cannon but, when they finally did, he told them he had already signed with the Rams. Still, the Oilers doubled the Rams' offer and Cannon verbally agreed to that contract as well. Cannon signed his contract with Houston on the field after the Sugar Bowl and then broke the bad news to the Rams in the locker room. Los Angeles sued because it had the first signed contract, but the courts sided with Houston, claiming Cannon was "exceptionally naive ... a provincial lad untutored and unwise in the ways of the business world."

2. Kevin Mawae was a great player at LSU, but he wasn't expected to be a high draft pick in the 1994 NFL draft. What ultimately earned Mawae his place in the second round was the final play of his college career in the regular season finale against Arkansas in 1993. The Tigers threw an interception at the one-yard line that Arkansas returned for a 99-yard touchdown. However, Mawae sprinted all the way down the field and made an effort to tackle the interceptor at LSU's

20-yard line. Though he missed on the play, Mawae said the Seattle staff was so impressed with his effort on the play that they persuaded the Seahawks to draft him.

3. Booger McFarland stayed at home in Louisiana with his mother for the 1999 NFL draft, choosing to relish the moment with his family. Reflecting on that day for ESPN ahead of the 2020 draft, McFarland said, "I'll never forget sitting in my mother's bedroom. I had an old prepaid PrimeCo cell phone, so the PrimeCo prepaid phone rings and it's an 813 number. I had no idea who it was, and it was the Tampa Bay Buccaneers, and it's the only time in my life I saw my mother cry. It was tears and joy. I don't care what else happens the rest of my life, I gave my mother that moment."

4. Josh Reed did a weekly blog post for NFL.com leading up to the 2001 NFL draft that went into detail about the draft process. In a post about his Pro Day performance, Reed said he was happy with his time in the 40-yard dash and the agility drills but felt he could have done better at route running and catching passes. Ultimately, the Bills drafted Reed in the second round.

5. For all of the issues JaMarcus Russell had in the NFL, there was no faulting the Raiders for using the first overall pick in 2007 on the quarterback. Russell impressed everyone at his Pro Day with his power and accuracy and Todd McShay called his passing session "the most impressive of all the pro days I've been to." Then the NFL Network draft analyst, Mike

Mayock, who is now coincidentally the Raiders' general manager, said a similar thing and still recalls Russell's Pro Day as arguably the best ever for a quarterback. That performance alone might have been enough to vault Russell from likely first rounder to the No. 1 overall pick.

6. Tyrann Mathieu was destined to be a top-10 pick in the 2013 NFL draft after his remarkable 2011 season as a sophomore for LSU. However, he lasted until the third round of the 2013 draft because of personal issues that prevented him from ever suiting up for the Tigers again. Mathieu was kicked off the team before the 2012 season due to a failed drug test, and he said during interviews before the draft that he "quit counting at 10" when asked about the number of drug tests he failed while at LSU. He ended up going to rehab and then passed the drug test at the NFL Combine. Arizona drafted him with the 69th pick that year.

7. Jarvis Landry suffered the crushing feeling of not being a first-round pick in a packed ballroom in Baton Rouge. The LSU receiver threw a giant party for friends and family for the first round of the 2014 draft, but he was not selected, and he ended up in his hotel room that night in tears. "I (was) just heartbroken," Landry said years later, reflecting on that day. "I felt like I didn't achieve my goal. I felt like I let my family down. I didn't know what Day 2 would be. I didn't know what Day 3 would be. I didn't know if I'd get drafted." Miami ended up drafting Landry in the second round with the 63rd pick, giving him a spot to begin his professional football career.

8. Leonard Fournette underwhelmed early at the NFL Combine when he showed up heavier than expected at 240 pounds and then had a 28.5-inch vertical jump. That meant there were a lot of eyes on him when he lined up to run the 40-yard dash, which he blazed through with ease at 4.51 seconds. That quick time was more than enough to quash the concerns about his athleticism, which was on better display in the agility and speed drills. The time in the 40-yard dash only proved to validate what scouts saw on tape at LSU despite Fournette looking much bigger than anticipated for a running back.

9. Derrius Guice had a lot of controversy surrounding him after he entered the 2018 draft. The running back went public with allegations that teams asked him about his sexual identity during interviews at the NFL Combine, but an NFL investigation revealed no proof of that occurring. Then, as the draft drew near, Guice had to begin answering questions about his personality and commitment. Rumors circulated that Guice was high-maintenance and was late to numerous meetings while at LSU, causing teams to pass over him in the first round of the draft. Washington eventually drafted Guice late in the second round, but the cloud of doubt hanging over the running back didn't subside for a little bit.

10. Joe Burrow had a unique draft day, thanks to the COVID-19 pandemic in the United States. The No. 1 overall pick was shipped a DIY broadcast set by the NFL so that they could feature the top prospects on the coverage of the draft.

Burrow wasn't tech-savvy enough to put it together, so he enlisted the help of his mother to help him assemble the setup for the draft.

CHAPTER 12:

WRITING THE RECORD BOOK

QUIZ TIME!

1. Which LSU offensive lineman holds the record for most starts with the Tigers?

    a. Ciron Black
    b. Rodney Reed
    c. Andrew Whitworth
    d. Kevin Mawae

2. How many yards did Kevin Faulk rush for in his LSU career?

    a. 4,387
    b. 4,431
    c. 4,557
    d. 4,662

3. Who holds the LSU record for most yards per game in a career?

    a. Derrius Guice
    b. Jeremy Hill

c. Leonard Fournette

d. Kevin Faulk

4. Kevin Faulk is the only player to have rushed for 40 rushing touchdowns in his LSU career.

   a. True

   b. False

5. Whose single-season record did Leonard Fournette break when he ran for 22 touchdowns in 2015?

   a. Jeremy Hill

   b. Charles Scott

   c. Dalton Hilliard

   d. LaBrandon Toefield

6. What is the LSU record for most passing attempts in a single game?

   a. 54

   b. 58

   c. 63

   d. 69

7. Before Joe Burrow tied the record with seven touchdown passes against Oklahoma, which team did LSU torch for seven combined touchdown passes in 1989?

   a. Kentucky

   b. Mississippi State

   c. Ohio

   d. Tulane

8. What was Joe Burrow's record-setting completion percentage in the 2019 season?

   a. 75.1 percent

   b. 76.3 percent

   c. 76.8 percent

   d. 77.4 percent

9. Anthony Jennings holds the LSU record for the longest pass with a 94-yard completion.

   a. True

   b. False

10. What is the LSU record for most consecutive completions, set by Joe Burrow during the 2019 season?

    a. 17

    b. 19

    c. 21

    d. 23

11. Who holds the record for most career receptions in LSU history?

    a. Michael Clayton

    b. Wendell Davis

    c. Brandon LaFell

    d. Justin Jefferson

12. How many catches did Justin Jefferson have in 2019 to set the single-season receptions record?

    a. 104

    b. 108

c. 111

d. 115

13. Who holds the LSU record with five touchdown catches in a game?

    a. Carlos Carson

    b. Devery Henderson

    c. Tony Moss

    d. Ja'Marr Chase

14. How long was Brandon LaFell's record streak of games with at least one catch?

    a. 34 games

    b. 36 games

    c. 39 games

    d. 41 games

15. Dwayne Bowe and Jarvis Landry share the record for most consecutive games with a touchdown catch at seven.

    a. True

    b. False

16. Who is LSU's all-time leading scorer?

    a. Cole Tracy

    b. Kevin Faulk

    c. David Browndyke

    d. Colt David

17. How many times has LSU tied the NCAA record with a 100-yard return for a touchdown?

a. 8

b. 9

c. 10

d. 11

18. Kevin Faulk is the only player in LSU history with 50 career touchdowns.

a. True

b. False

19. Who is not one of the three kickers to have made a 54-yard field goal to stand equal as LSU's record-holder?

a. Cole Tracy

b. Wade Richey

c. Colt David

d. Ron Lewis

20. How long was Donnie Jones' punt in 2002 to set the record for the longest punt in LSU history?

a. 72 yards

b. 77 yards

c. 81 yards

d. 86 yards

QUIZ ANSWERS

1. A – Ciron Black

2. C – 4,557

3. C – Leonard Fournette

4. B – False

5. D – LaBrandon Toefield

6. D – 69

7. C – Ohio

8. B – 76.3 percent

9. A – True

10. A – 17

11. B – Wendell Davis

12. C – 111

13. A – Carlos Carson

14. D – 41 games

15. A – True

16. D – Colt David

17. B – 9

18. B – False

19. C – Colt David

20. D – 86 yards

DID YOU KNOW?

1. LSU had just two left tackles over an eight-season stretch from 2002 through 2009 as a pair of stud offensive linemen controlled the blindside for the Tigers. Andrew Whitworth set the LSU record with 52 consecutive starts from 2002-2005, missing just one practice his entire career, and that was to attend his graduation ceremony. He was replaced by Ciron Black, who went on to start 53 straight games for the Tigers and break Whitworth's record.

2. On Sept. 10, 1994, Eddie Kennison ran himself into the NCAA record book even if it wasn't the smartest football play in the world. Mississippi State punted the ball to LSU, and it skipped at the 4-yard line and hopped into the end zone. Instincts took over for Kennison, who failed to cleanly field the punt and began the return six yards deep in his own end zone. Somehow, the speedster found an escape route from the Bulldogs defenders and ran for a 100-yard TD return, a record that cannot be broken under modern NCAA rules, which list every punt return touchdown from the end zone as 100 yards.

3. On the day Kevin Faulk set the school record with five rushing touchdowns, he wasn't the only running back who had success that day. LSU ran for 400 yards and tied a school record with eight rushing touchdowns against Kentucky on November 1, 1997. Faulk ran for 212 yards while Rondell

Mealey added 131 rushing yards and two scores in the game and quarterback Herb Tyler scored the eighth rushing touchdown. It was the second time that Faulk and Mealey ran for 100 yards in the same game after doing so the previous season against Houston.

4. It was unfortunately in a losing effort, but Tommy Hodson was the only LSU player in the 20th century to throw for 400 yards in a game. Hodson threw for 438 yards and four touchdowns in a 45-39 loss to Tennessee at Tiger Stadium. Perhaps more impressive was the fact Hodson did not throw an interception in 49 attempts, a record later tied by Joe Burrow in the Peach Bowl. His first touchdown pass that day was his 58th at LSU, setting the school record he still holds.

5. Jesse Daigle started only six games in his LSU career, but Todd Kinchen almost single-handedly made sure Daigle's name would be in the record books 30 years after his career ended. The receiver held the school record for 10 years with 248 receiving yards in LSU's loss to Mississippi State in 1991. Kinchen needed to make only nine catches to amass that total, which also was the SEC record at the time. He started strong with a 75-yard touchdown catch on the second play of the game. Daigle threw for 394 yards that day and also had 6 rushing yards. That was one of 10 games in LSU history in which the quarterback had at least 400 yards of total offense.

6. An LSU player has had three sacks in a game many times, but only Chuck Wiley has done it four times in for the

Tigers. In 1995 against South Carolina, Wiley had four of LSU's seven sacks in the game in a game that would turn out to be historic for other reasons. Wiley had eight tackles, including five for losses totaling 30 yards, 29 of which came on the sacks. Of course, most people know that game as the last tie in SEC history as LSU and South Carolina tied 20-20 the year before endless overtime was instituted in FBS football.

7. There is something special about the letter C and intercepting passes for LSU. The last five players to tie the school record for interceptions in a game all had names beginning with the letter C. In addition, five of the six players with at least seven interceptions in a season for the Tigers have names beginning with the letter C. Craig Burns, Corey Webster, and Chris Williams are the only three players to be on both lists. Craig Steltz and Clinton Burrell both had three interceptions in a game while Cedric Donaldson had seven interceptions in 1997.

8. Cole Tracy is the NCAA's all-time leading scorer across all divisions with 502 points, including an NCAA record 97 field goals. Most of those points came at Division II Assumption College in Massachusetts, but his final year at LSU was one for the record books as well. He tied the school record with a 54-yard field goal in his LSU debut against Miami to open the 2018 season and then tied another record with five made field goals against Georgia. Tracy set the LSU single-game scoring record for a kicker in that game with 18 total points against the Bulldogs, and he set the

Tigers record with 29 made field goals in his one season in Baton Rouge.

9. There were a lot of impressive moments in Joe Burrow's 2019 season, but his accuracy might have been the most impressive of them all. Burrow set LSU records for passing attempts with 527 and completions with 402 while still obliterating LSU's completion percentage record by more than 8 points. Burrow completed 71 percent or more of his passes in every game except the national championship game to set the SEC record at 76.3 percent. That boosted his two-year completion percentage to 68.5 percent, which is also an LSU record.

10. LSU and Texas A&M played the highest-scoring football game in NCAA history in 2018 when the Aggies defeated the Tigers 74-72 in seven overtimes. It dropped LSU's record to 8-7 in overtime games and the contest was the fifth ever to enter a seventh extra period. Both teams kicked field goals in the first and fourth overtimes, but otherwise scored touchdowns in every other period. The mandatory two-point conversions were successful in the third and sixth overtime periods, but Texas A&M also converted on the two-point conversion in the seventh to sneak out with a win at home.

CONCLUSION

Congratulations on finishing this book and reaching the end of a journey that hopefully tested your knowledge of LSU football. If we've done our jobs well, you've reached this point filled to the brim with facts about your favorite college football program, the LSU Tigers. Whether it's information about the days before you became a fan or facts about the behind-the-scenes interactions that led to your favorite moments, we hope you enjoyed this trip through the history of the Tigers.

From their loss in the first game to Tulane, through the confetti falling in New Orleans in January 2020, Louisiana State University has provided the citizens of Baton Rouge and its many other fans with plenty of exciting moments on the gridiron. Fans have experienced the thrill of three national championships over the past 20 years and the heartbreak of championship opportunities gone by but, through it all, the purple and gold pride has shone deeply on the bayou. There have been some sensational players who have come through LSU's program and several others you would probably rather forget. Some of the best coaches in the history of college football were at the helm of the Tigers, and some coaching regimes weren't as successful. But, through it all, LSU has found success on the field in a difficult conference.

We designed this book for you, the fans, to be able to embrace your favorite team and feel closer to them. Maybe you weren't familiar with what happened in LSU football before you became a student or fan. Perhaps you've lost touch with your alma mater in recent years, or you just wanted to re-live the glory days. This book was simply meant for enjoyment and sharing knowledge, so no matter if you aced the quizzes, or were stumped by them all, we hope you have fun and leave with more pride for the Tigers.

The 2020 season provided its fair share of challenges for coach Ed Orgeron, but the Tigers also showed plenty of spark in a tough year. This is a program that has never stayed dormant for long, and Orgeron's passion for the school isn't stopping anytime soon. Under Coach O, the Tigers will be back competing toe-to-toe with Alabama and the rest of the SEC and there will be players on the national stage every season. The next great Tigers star might already be on campus or maybe the coaching staff is getting set to recruit him now. But, as long as LSU football exists, the Tigers will always be a force to be reckoned with on the gridiron.

Made in the USA
Columbia, SC
15 November 2024

46638680R00076